C0-AWL-550

MANUSCRIPTS OF
LEONARDO DA VINCI

MANUSCRIPTS OF
LEONARDO da VINCI

THEIR HISTORY, WITH A DESCRIPTION OF
THE MANUSCRIPT EDITIONS IN FACSIMILE

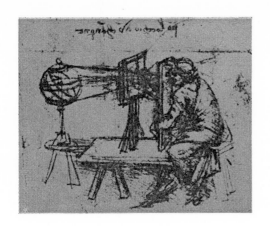

THE ELMER BELT LIBRARY OF VINCIANA
LOS ANGELES : CALIFORNIA : MCMXLVIII

Catalogue by Kate Trauman Steinitz
with the assistance of Margot Archer

ANDERSON & RITCHIE : THE WARD RITCHIE PRESS

Table of Contents

WHAT HAPPENED TO LEONARDO DA VINCI'S MANUSCRIPTS

A picture story drawn by Kate Steinitz

THE STORY OF
THE MANUSCRIPTS

The Story of the Manuscripts
ELMER BELT

ONE OF THE GREAT MIRACLES in man's conflict with oblivion is the preservation of Leonardo's notebook manuscripts. The rough journals which Leonardo kept throughout most of his adult life he intended as a matter-of-fact record with which to jog his own memory. These factual expressions, however, produced a simple prose of great strength and beauty.

The material contained in these notebooks was hidden from most men by two factors: first, the right-to-left script, or mirror writing, natural to Leonardo because of his left-handedness and unintentionally cryptic to most persons who saw the notes; and secondly, the obscure dialect of Leonardo's birthplace, in which the notes were written. These two difficulties stood in the way of a ready understanding of the content of the notebooks.

The beautiful drawings which fill the pages are in many cases simply singularly effective mechanical drawings often seeming to suggest entirely new mechanical designs, but probably more often rescuing old designs from oblivion because of being reproduced by Leonardo. Included also were trial drawings of Leonardo's great paintings, these little sketches themselves often proving to be more appealing and moving in their design than the great paintings which grew from them.

Much of the seven thousand pages of this material remaining to us has been transliterated into modern Italian. A large amount of this transliterated material has been translated into French and German, less in English. There is still much of it, although readily available in the original, locked away from the inquiring minds of moderns because of the slow labor required for its translation.

In the period immediately following Leonardo, it was virtually all a closed book. Yet men treasured these beautiful but cryptic pages, then as now, for the sheer wonder of their drawings and for what the mysterious text might contain. Each new owner sought not to have them perish and as his period of custody drew to an end endeavored to seek out a place of safety for them. Their amazing course through history forms a beautiful story of man's unselfish desire to preserve things of value for his successors.

Our first and only glimpse of this tremendous series of notebooks in its intact state is seen through the eyes of the journal-keeping Antonio de Beatis, who on October 10, 1517, visited Leonardo, then old and suffering from a recent stroke which had partially paralyzed his left side. In the company of Cardinal Luigi d'Aragon, Beatis visited Leonardo at Cloux. To these men, Leonardo displayed his possessions and talked about them. De Beatis reports:

He has composed a remarkable anatomy with pictorial demonstrations of limbs, muscles, veins, nerves, joints, intestines, and whatever one could imagine, men as well as women, such as never have been made before by any person. This is what we have seen with our own eyes. And he said that he had dissected more than 30 bodies of men and women of all ages. He has also composed works on the nature of water and machines, and other matters and accordingly has put this down in an infinite number of volumes all in the vulgar tongue which if published would be most useful and enjoyable.

Two years later in 1519, Leonardo died. By his will, all of his manuscripts and drawings passed into the possession of Francesco Melzi, his much-loved pupil and long-time associate. Melzi, a wealthy Milanese artist, brought the manuscripts back to Milan and kept them in his villa in Vaprio. Between 1537 and 1545 Melzi was visited by an able writer, the so-called Anonymous Gaddianus, or Anonymous Fiorentino. He reports in a manuscript, the Codex Magliabechianus, XVII, 17, now in the National Library in Florence:

4

Leonardo left Milan, entering the service of King Francis. He took many of his drawings along to France and he left in his testament to Francesco Melzi, a Milanese gentleman, all his money, panels, books, writings, drawings, instruments and likenesses, everything relating to painting, art and industry which remained; and he made him the executor of his testament.

In his great Life of Leonardo, 1568, Vasari tells of his visit to Melzi's house. In referring to the anatomic manuscripts, he writes of the young anatomist Marc' Antonio as a Leonardo collaborator in anatomy, and he states:

In this attempt Marc' Antonio was wonderfully aided by the genius and labour of Leonardo, who filled a book of drawings in red crayon, outlined with the pen, all copies made with the utmost care [from bodies] dissected by his own hand. In this book he set forth the entire structure, arrangement, and disposition of the bones, to which he afterwards added all the nerves, in their due order, and next supplied the muscles, of which the first are affixed to the bones, the second give the power of cohesion or holding firmly, and the third impart that of motion. Of each separate part he wrote an explanation in rude characters, written backwards and with the left-hand, so that whoever is not practised in reading cannot understand them, since they are only to be read with a mirror. Of these anatomical drawings of the human form, a great part is now in the possession of Messer Francesco da Melzo, a Milanese gentleman, who, in the time of Leonardo, was a child of remarkable beauty, much beloved by him, and is now a handsome and amiable old man, who sets great store by these drawings, and treasures them as relics, together with the portrait of Leonardo of blessed memory. To all who read these writings it must appear almost incredible that this sublime genius could, at the same time, discourse, as he has done, of art, and of the muscles, nerves, veins and every other part of the frame, all treated with equal diligence and success. There are, besides, certain other writings of Leonardo, also written with the left-hand, in the possession of N. N. (probably Aurelio Luini), a painter of Milan; they treat of painting, of design generally, and of colouring. This artist came to see me in Florence no long time since; he then had an intention of publishing this work, and took it with him to Rome, there to give this purpose effect, but what was the end of the matter I do not know. (Translation: Blashfield and Hopkins.)

In 1570, two years after this account was written, Francesco Melzi died and left his property to his relative, Orazio Melzi, a doctor of law. Just before Francesco Melzi's death, he had also been visited by the Milanese painter, Lomazzo, who wrote about this visit twenty years later in his *Idea del Tempio della Pittura*, 1590, as follows:

Before all others, Leonardo is worth remembering as he taught the Anatomy of the human body and of horses which I have seen at Francesco Melzi, drawn divinely by Leonardo's hands. He also demonstrated in figures all proportions of the limbs of the human body. He wrote on the perspective of light and how to draw the main forms of nature and books on many more subjects . . . but of all these works none was printed, existing only in his manuscripts which to a great part, have come into the hands of Pompeo Leoni, a sculptor of the Catholic King of Spain, who had them from a relative of Francesco Melzi, and some also came into the hands of Signor Guido Mazenta, distinguished scholar who treasured them lovingly.

Lomazzo's account is the first hint of the dispersal of these treasures by the house of Melzi through the action of Doctor of Law Orazio Melzi. The theft of many of the manuscripts by Aldus Manutius' nephew, Lelio Gavardi d'Asola, admitted to the Melzi household as a tutor; the attempted return of the stolen goods by a law student, Ambrosio Mazenta; Orazio's refusal to accept the returned manuscripts followed by his sudden realization of their value, after the Mazenta brothers had exhibited them to appreciative artists; and the ultimate return of seven of the manuscripts to the Melzis by Mazenta, all is told in an excellently written report by Ambrosio Mazenta which he set down at the end of his life between 1631 and 1635. This account states that, when Ambrosio Mazenta studied law in Pisa in 1588, another student, Lelio Gavardi d'Asola, showed him 13 notebooks of Leonardo. Gavardi was a nephew

6

of Aldus Manutius and had been a tutor in the house of Orazio Melzi. When he left in order to study law he had slyly taken along 13 manuscripts with the intention of selling them to the Grand Duke of Florence. However, the Grand Duke died before Gavardi was able to show him the manuscripts. Mazenta reproached Gavardi for his conduct and persuaded Gavardi to let him return them; however, Orazio Melzi was not eager to accept them, as in his villa he kept many more books and other relics of this master, Leonardo. The brothers Mazenta then kept the manuscripts and showed them to many famous artists who also begged Dr. Melzi for some of the Leonardo material. The person most eager to acquire Leonardo's drawings was Pompeo Leoni, sculptor, pupil of Michelangelo, in the service of the King of Spain. He promised Melzi honors and privileges in the Senate of Milan if he would enable him to make a present of this material to the King of Spain, who was an ardent collector of such singularities as Leonardo's work. Orazio Melzi, who had so shortly before paid little attention to Leonardo's work, now implored the Mazentas to return the manuscripts. Generously, the brothers Mazenta returned seven of them to Melzi, who gave much of this material to Pompeo Leoni.

Of the Mazenta brothers' remaining six manuscripts, a treatise on light and shadow, later marked C by Venturi, was given to Cardinal Federigo Borromeo, who gave it to the Ambrosian Library, which he founded in 1603. This manuscript remained there until 1796, when Napoleon transferred it to the Institut de France.

Two of Mazentas' six manuscripts were ultimately lost—one they had given to the painter Figgino, the other to the Duke of Savoy. Ambrogio Figgino, or Figini, bequeathed his manuscript to Ercole Bianchi. It then came into the possession of the English consul, Joseph Smith. With the sale of Smith's property in 1759, all record of the manuscript ends. Nothing is known of the history of the other manuscript which was given to

Duke Carlo Emanuele of Savoy. Professor Govi states his belief that it was burned in one of the fires which damaged the Turin library in 1667 or 1679.

Thus the Mazentas retained three of Leonardo's manuscripts. After Guido Mazenta's death, Pompeo Leoni came into possession of these three remaining notebooks. Possibly also he had received even more material from Orazio Melzi. Leoni undid the original notebooks and mounted the leaves in paper frames so that both sides of the leaves could be seen. These large paper frames or mats he assembled haphazardly without any chronological sequence and bound them in two large volumes.

One of these volumes Pompeo Leoni took to Spain in 1591. In Spain, he sold it to Don Juan d'Espina. This was the body of the manuscripts now in the British Isles. The path of their journey to England can be traced only partly, but it is known that most of them were purchased by Thomas Howard, Earl of Arundel, Marshal of England, while traveling in Spain and Italy. Thomas Howard also made purchases through agents in Holland and Germany for his own collections and for the English Crown. Writing to Lord Aston, January 19, 1636, he complains about Don Juan d'Espina's obstinacies in the proceedings of the sale.

The Codex Arundel is now in the British Museum. A note in John Evelyn's diary, January 9, 1666, states that Evelyn persuaded the heir of this treasure, who had little inclination for books, to give the codex to the Royal Society. This was done in 1681. In 1831 it was transferred to the British Museum.

The other volume compiled by Pompeo Leoni from approximately ten different notebooks is known as the Codex Atlanticus. Pompeo Leoni did not present it to the King of Spain as he first intended, but brought it back to Italy where he left it to his heir, Cleodoro Calchi.

John Evelyn, in his memoirs, noted that King Charles of England offered 1,000 English pounds for the Codex Atlanticus

LARGE CANNON BEING RAISED. THE ILLUSTRATION MARKS THE BIRTH OF THE
MACHINE AGE, SHOWING MECHANICALLY CONSTRUCTED DUPLICATE SPARE
PARTS STORED IN RESERVE FOR REPLACEMENT.

Windsor 12647, Reale Commissione Vinciana 83. Drawn about 1485-88.

THE HALL OF LEONARDO DA VINCI IN THE AMBROSIAN LIBRARY, MILAN.

RAVASCO'S ROCK CRYSTAL CHEST, THE PRESENT REPOSITORY OF THE CODEX ATLANTICUS.

through the Lord Marshal, Thomas Howard, Earl of Arundel. However, the Codex Atlanticus was no longer available for any amount of money. It was in the possession of the Italian patriot, Count Galeazzo Arconati, who had bought it for 300 gold scudi from Pompeo Leoni's heir, Calchi, intending to save this treasure for Italy. The Count's collection contained a number of smaller notebooks which he had already acquired, probably also from Pompeo Leoni, but the Codex Atlanticus was the greatest volume in his collection. In 1636 Count Galeazzo Arconati made his great donation to the Ambrosian Library. The deeds of the donation are dated 1637. Twelve manuscripts are enumerated and described:

1. Codex Atlanticus. "The first is a great book which is 13 *oncie* long and 9½ *oncie* wide, covered with red leather and stamped with two gold borders and four coats-of-arms with eagles and lions . . . with gold letters DISEGNI DI MACHINE ET DELLE ARTI SECRETI, E ALTRE COSE DI LEONARDO DA VINCI, RACCOLTI DA POMPEO LEONI . . ."

2. Manuscript copy of Luca Paciolo's Divina Proportione, written about 1497, a manuscript so beautiful that Cardinal Federigo Borromeo, who had founded the library, is said to have kissed it in admiration. The book is written on parchment and may contain original drawings by Leonardo da Vinci. There is, however, another manuscript of this text in Geneva which can compete with it in beauty.

3. "A book in quarto bound in parchment on the spine of which, one reads, 'Di Leonardo da Vincie.' It is of 100 leaves, but lacking the first; on the second, one sees some fruit of *marene*. In the body of this volume are inserted 5 folios with various designs, mostly javelins. At the end of this volume, another little volume with various mathematical figures and birds, 18 leaves, is sewn to the parchment cover." This description fits the codices now known

9

as Codex *B*, on the birds' flight, and Ashburnham 2037, representing a section of Manuscript *B*. It deals with the architecture of fortifications, city planning, the helicopter, the flying machine, and other subjects.

4. Manuscript *A* (at that time complete with the section now known as Codex Ashburnham 2038). The codex and its lost sections are now in the Institut de France. "The fourth is a book of same size and quality, covered with parchment . . . with 114 leaves . . . and on the spine the words DI LEONARDO DA VINCI and on the front cover LEONAR."

5. "The 5th is another similar book bound in quarto, as the above, having 54 leaves. On the first leaves are some grotesque drawings of heads. Inscribed on the spine is LEONARDO DA VINCI." This is the codex which Don Carlo Trivulzio bought from Gaetano Caccia of Novara. It had been removed, possibly by Arconati himself, from the Ambrosian Library in exchange for Manuscript *D*, which contained the treatise on the eye. The removed manuscript went to the library of Prince Trivulzio in Milan, who bequeathed it to the Castello Sforzesco, where it resides.

6. The manuscripts now known as *E*, with notes on the birds' flight, mechanism of gravity, plant physiology and an account of the deluge. "The sixth is a book in octavo covered with old white boards with the note on the cover 'the leaves are correct 96, which means ninety-six' and below a capital B . . ."

7. The manuscript now known as *F* on water and landscapes. "The seventh is another similar book . . . bound in boards of ninety-six leaves, the first of which has a mathematical figure at the margin of the verso. On the fly-leaf is written in capitals LEONAR." Ravaisson-Mollien states that the marking LEONAR has since been effaced.

8. Manuscript now known as *G*. "Another book bound in boards in octavo with 96, ninety-six, leaves except the lacking which is the seventh and the eighteenth with its conjugate 31; on top written LEONAR . . . on the first and last leaves . . . is confirmed that the afore-mentioned leaves 7, 18 and 31 are lacking."

9. Manuscripts *H*1, *H*2, and *H*3, bound in one volume containing animal fables and studies in physiology. "The ninth is a book in *sedecimo* in parchment. On the spine one sees written DI LEONARDO DA VINCI and on top in capitals LEONAR."

10. Manuscripts *I*1 and *I*2, bound in one volume dealing with oil fresco material and containing quotations from earlier authors and notes in a secret language. "The tenth is another one similar in size and binding, of 91 leaves. On the spine is written DI LEONARDO DA VINCI . . . On the last leaf is a mathematical figure with various letters and a drawing of a helmeted head in sanguine."

11. Manuscript now known as *L* on flight, containing a sketch for the Last Supper and a sketch of a fortress. "The eleventh is another book in *sedecimo* bound in turkish blue old boards which has at the bottom in capital letters the word LEONAR. Of ninety-four leaves, the first of which shows mathematical designs . . ."

12. Manuscript now known as *M* on geometry and mechanics, anecdotes and fables. "The twelfth is only a book in *sedecimo* covered in plain yellowed boards. It has no fly leaf and only the 94 leaves on the first of which are various figures and triangles . . ."

At a later date, 1674, Count Orazio Archinti donated three small Leonardo notebooks to the Ambrosian Library now known as manuscripts *K*1, *K*2, and *K*3.

When Napoleon entered Milan with his victorious army in 1796, he declared: "All men of genius, all who have attained distinction in the Republic of Letters are French, whatever be the country which has given them birth." Judged by this standard, Leonardo da Vinci's manuscripts in the Ambrosiana were French and were packed for transmission to France. On the long journey, the two cases in which the Leonardo materials were packed were separated from one another. The one containing the Codex Atlanticus arrived at the Bibliothèque Nationale, the one containing the smaller manuscripts reached the Institut de France.

After Wellington conquered Napoleon at Waterloo, the Duke ordered the restitution of properties stolen by the French. The Allied governments endorsed the Italian claim to the Vincian material.

The Austrian Baron of Ottenfels was charged with the restoration of the manuscripts to Italy. The Baron was not particularly meticulous in the performance of his duty and instead of manuscripts *A* to *K* and Ashburnham 2037 and 2038, several handwritten copies were sent to Italy. These are the manuscripts *H* 227, 228, 229 inf., now at the Ambrosian Library. The originals remained in the Institut de France, where they are today. The Codex Atlanticus, however, arrived in the Ambrosiana in 1815, at the end of the year. In 1938, the museum authorities honored it with a beautiful marble and glass case placed in an elaborate exhibition hall in the Ambrosian Library.

In addition to the Codex Arundel now in England which Thomas Howard, Earl of Arundel, bought from Don Juan d'Espina in Spain, there is another manuscript in the South Kensington Museum, bequeathed to it by John Forster in 1876. John Forster had received the Codex Forster from his friend, Lord Lytton, who had bought it in Vienna.

The codex in the possession of Lord Leicester, Holkham Hall, Norfolk, most probably was acquired by Thomas Coke,

First Earl of Leicester, who spent several years in Rome before 1775. An added title page shows evidence of its possession by the painter, Giuseppe Ghezzi, who lived in Rome in the first part of the 18th century.

Another part of the material which Pompeo Leoni assembled came to light in England in Windsor Castle about 1778. About that time, the opening of an old chest found in Kensington Palace took place. The report by Charles Rogers given in "A Collection of Prints in Imitation of Drawings" states: "This great curiosity . . . was deposited by King Charles himself in a large and strong chest in which it lay unobserved and forgotten for 120 years until Mr. Dalton, Royal Librarian, fortunately discovered it on the bottom of the same chest in the beginning of the reign of his present majesty . . . , a treasure for its riches rivalling even that of Milan the great." Charles Rogers then describes the volume of 234 leaves containing 779 drawings. On the cover was the description: "DISEGNI.DI.LEONARDO.DA.VINCI.RESTAURATI.DA.POMPEO.LEONI"

After the discovery, the greatest number of the drawings were mounted and exhibited in Grosvenor Palace under the sponsorship and supervision of the Prince Consort. The anatomic drawings were not mounted. In 1784 the great anatomist and surgeon William Hunter reported in his lectures his profound impressions upon viewing these anatomic drawings of Leonardo which the Royal Librarian, Mr. Dalton, had brought to his attention and allowed him to study.

In 1930, after all of the anatomic drawings had been published, they were bound into three volumes, and they remain in Windsor Castle.

LEONARDO DA VINCI'S MANUSCRIPTS AND THEIR EDITIONS IN FAC-SIMILE.

PRIOR to the emergence of facsimile editions of Leonardo's notebooks very few scholars had the opportunity of studying

Leonardo's original manuscripts. Very little of this true source material was accessible. Leonardo's drawings and some of his scientific studies were in circulation in more-or-less correct reproductions made by the engravers: Wenceslaus Hollar, Comte de Caylus, Giuseppe Gerli and others.

With the advent of the art of lithography, a beautiful facsimile of selected sheets of Leonardo's text and drawings from the Codex Atlanticus appeared as the *Saggio delle Opere di Leonardo da Vinci*, Milan, 1872. This was the first of a host of careful reproductions which were to follow. Each is in our library and we have carefully described them here. In the aggregate they now make available to scholars the whole of the known Leonardo notebook material with the exception of a dozen or so desultory sheets housed separately in libraries scattered throughout Europe. This is primary source material in the study of Leonardo and his work. These foundation stones, gathered in one place, are now more readily available to American scholars for study than are the scattered originals in European libraries. Our bibliography of this material follows.

THE CATALOGUE OF
THE FACSIMILE EDITIONS

The Codex Atlanticus

*Facsimile editions of Codex Atlanticus, 1872, 1894, to 1904,
Indices, Dizionario.*

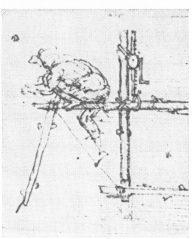

SAGGIO [red] / DELLE OPERE / DI / LEONARDO DA VINCI [red] /
[short line] / CON VENTIQUATTRO TAVOLE FOTOLITOGRAFICHE DI
SCRITTURE E DISEGNI / TRATTI DAL / CODICE ATLANTICO [red] /
[printer's flower] / MILANO / [red] / TITO DI GIOVANNI RICORDI-
IMPRESSE / MDCCCLXXII / (EDIZIONE DI 300 ESEMPLARI). [red]

DESCRIPTION: Frontispiece portrait of Leonardo; vii, 32 pages; [51]
leaves with alternate 24 plates and text. The text consists of a comprehensive transcription of Leonardo's text facing the respective
plate, and on recto of the text leaves, a caption and brief explanation of it by Giuseppe Colombo. Size: 54.5 x 37.5 cm.

*The copy in the Belt Library is No. 244 of 300 copies. Binding:
Tooled ¾ calf, marbled boards.*

This edition gave the impetus to all modern Vincian editions
in facsimile. It was planned by a commission appointed by
Cesare Correnti, Ministro della Istruzione Pubblica, and edited

17

with essays by Belgiojoso, Mongeri, Govi and Boito, members of the commission.

The leaves here presented in facsimile were again reproduced in the great edition of the Codex Atlanticus, Milan, Hoepli, 1894-1904.

IL / CODICE ATLANTICO [red] / DI / LEONARDO DA VINCI / NELLA BIBLIOTECA AMBROSIANA / DI MILANO / RIPRODOTTO E PUBBLICATO / DALLA / REGIA ACCADEMIA DEI LINCEI [red] / SOTTO GLI AUSPICI E COL SUSSIDIO / DEL RE E DEL GOVERNO / [Lincei coat-of-arms: lynx surrounded by wreath surmounted by a crown] / ULRICO HOEPLI [red] / EDITORE-LIBRAIO DELLA REAL CASA E DELLA R. ACCADEMIA DEI LINCEI / MILANO / [short line] / MDCCCLXXXXIV [to MCMIV]

DESCRIPTION: XIV, 1311 pages with preface by Fr. Brioschi, president of the Academy of the Lincei, and literal and critical transcriptions by Piumati. 1384 plates with facsimiles of 401 folios of the codex, each containing one or more manuscript sheets of various sizes. They are printed on verso and recto of the leaves.

Text and plates are separated. This arrangement permits juxtaposition, while examining the plates, with any of the transcriptions, which often run through several pages. Size: 52 x 37 cm.

The edition is limited to 280 copies. The material is assembled in fasciculi. The paper has unusual and obvious watermarks: top center of the page is a lynx, bottom center the date 1887, bottom on one side of page-fold a P and on the side of fold M, centered on the inner and outer margins the letters L V intertwined.

The two sets in the Belt Library are: No. 244 assembled in 35 fasciculi, each being a portfolio with plates and the corresponding section of transcriptions sewn into the wrappers. On the front wrapper the text of the title page is repeated, inside the back wrapper and verso the publishing program and prices.

Number 262 is assembled in 12 portfolios, six containing the text only and six containing the plates. Each portfolio has a title page, however, no special wrappers around the text.

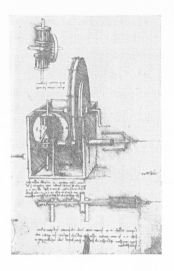

The story of Codex Atlanticus is contained in D. Ambrosio Mazenta's famous "Memorie." In this report, written between 1631 and 1635, Mazenta tells the story of Gavardi d'Asola's theft of the manuscripts and of his own futile attempt to restore the 13 stolen manuscripts to the legal owner, Orazio Melzi. Then, finding himself in the possession of the notebooks, he and his brothers exhibited them to the public in a "pomposa mostra." Hearing how easily the collection was acquired, many visitors of the show tried to get relics from Leonardo's studio. One of these treasure-hunters was the sculptor Pompeo Leoni, pupil of Michelangelo, then in the service of King Philip II of Spain. He promised Melzi honors and offices in the senate of Milan if he could get possession of Mazenta's manuscripts. He would then donate the treasure to the King of Spain, who was a passionate collector of such singularities. Doctor Melzi, who had shown no interest in Leonardo's works, now implored Mazenta, on his knees, to restore his gift, and courteously the brothers Mazenta returned seven of the books. Of the remaining six, one was given to the Cardinal Borromeo, another to the painter Figino, a third to Duke Emanuel of Savoy. There were still three notebooks in the possession of the Mazentas, which after Guido Mazenta's death also came into Pompeo Leoni's hands. Pompeo Leoni then compiled and mounted his material, assembling it in two giant volumes. He finished his compilation probably around 1589. The one which is now in Windsor Castle was acquired by Don Juan d'Espina in Spain; the other, the Codex Atlanticus, was not given to King Philip II. It was still in Leoni's possession when he returned to Italy in 1604, and passed, after his death, to his heir, Cleodoro Calchi. From Calchi, the Italian patriot Count Galeazzo Arconati bought the codex for 300 gold *scudi* and kept it as a priceless treasure not available for money. He resisted the negotiations made by the Earl of Arundel. An offer of a thousand *doppie d'oro* from the English Crown made to Arconati in 1630 through Jacomo Antonio Annone was also turned down. Annone certified this in a letter of 1636. This letter is published in Uzielli, *Ricerche*, 1884, page 248.

In 1636, Arconati presented his manuscripts of Leonardo to the Ambrosian Library. The deed of this gift is dated 21 January, 1637. The first entry in this deed is *Il Codice Atlantico*. The donation included Leonardo's manuscripts now called *A, B, E, F, G, H, I, L, M* and the codex on the birds' flight.

Napoleon Bonaparte with his army entered Milan, May 15, 1796, and four days later took possession of certain monuments of science and art, in order to bring them to Paris for "protective custody." Leonardo's manuscripts were included.

On the long voyage, which lasted until November, 1796, the case containing 12 small manuscripts and case number 19 labeled "carton des ouvrages de Léonard de Vinci" containing the Codex Atlanticus were separated by mistake. Codex Atlanticus arrived at the Bibliothèque Nationale, the manuscripts at the Institut de France. This separation was probably the reason why the manuscripts were not restored to Italy when the

Codex Atlanticus was returned to the Ambrosiana after Napoleon's defeat in 1815, as a result of the restitution order of the Duke of Wellington. The Codex Atlanticus is now kept in the Sala di Leonardo of the Ambrosiana, which was opened with great ceremonies in March 1938. The volume can be seen in a huge case of rock crystal and steel with bands of gold and lapis-lazuli, made and donated by Alfredo Ravasco. It is placed upon a huge table of multi-colored marble wide enough to carry two showcases of crystal in which some of the precious leaves are displayed. The cover carries in golden letters the title: DISEGNI. DI. MACHINE. ET. / DELLE. ARTI. SECRETI. / ET. ALTRE. COSE. / DI LEONARDO DA VINCI / RACOLTI DA / POMPEO LEO / NI /

The original codex, as seen through the transparent walls of its case, is a volume of 65 x 45 cm., 1222 pages, composed of loose sheets of various sizes, each of the folios containing one or more leaves of the original manuscript, altogether 1600, with 1750 drawings and text written on verso and recto. The leaves are mounted into paper frames so that recto and verso can be seen. The numbering indicates only the number of these mountings. They are used in this publication of 1894 of the Codex Atlanticus.

The ten notebooks of Leonardo which Pompeo Leoni used for his great compilation were written between 1483 and 1518, thus it contains documents from all periods of Leonardo's activities since maturity and personal entries which are helpful in dating his studies. Pompeo Leoni's sequence of arrangement, however, was haphazard. Generations of scholars searched their way through the maze of material trying to interpret it and to place it in logical order. When the work was published in the facsimile edition the indices were still no more than a project. They were only published after 10 years of pathfinding through the labyrinth of this material.

The name Codex Atlanticus was given to this volume because of its giant size. The title on the cover indicates that the majority of the contents is scientific in character and deals with mechanics and machinery. In *Guida sommaria dell' Ambrosiana*, 1907, by Achille Ratti (later Pope Pius XI), these subjects are enumerated: In military engineering, designs of artillery anticipating the most modern applications, studies in fortification, battle ships, with reference to a steamship; in astronomy, observations on the movement of the earth; in physics and chemistry, various observations of gravity, equilibrium, light, sound, and qualities and combinations of bodies; in hydraulics, various machines to raise water, drawings and studies of navigable canals; in geometry, sketches of figures for the treatise *Divina Proportione* by Luca Paciolo; in geodesy, studies for measuring the surface of the earth; in cartography, sketches in relief for places and areas; in mechanics, designs for tools and machines for flying, and others, including the automobile, submarine, diving devices and many suggestions of rational methods of how to make pavements, locks and keys, tools such as pliers, textile and metallurgical machines. There are architectural plans for churches and other buildings, cupolas and monuments; studies of perspective and precepts for painters, sketches of landscapes and sketches for the *Adoration of the Magi* in San Giovanni; sketches for the monument of Francesco Sforza, sketches for the *Leda*, and for the famous portrait of Beatrice d'Este.

The codex contains also the draft for the famous letter of application to Lodovico Sforza, written right to left, and several other notes and letters written in the normal fashion from left to right. Piumati doubted that any of these entries on the leaves were written by Leonardo and therefore he omitted the transcription of them in his edition. Several scholars were doubtful about the Sforza letter. Beltrami published an essay *La "destra mano" di Leonardo da Vinci e le lacune nella edizione del Codice Atlantico*, Milano-Roma, Alfieri &

22

Lacroix, Volume II of *Analecta Ambrosiana* [1919], to offer evidence that at least most of the notes from right to left were by Leonardo. These *lacunae*, gaps, in the transcription were supplied in Galbiati's *"Dizionario Leonardesco,"* Milan, 1939. For reasons unknown, Piumati also omitted three sheets of Codex Atlanticus which were published in the *Dizionario,* 1939, in facsimile.

INDICI [red] / PER MATERIE ED ALFABETICO / DEL / CODICE ATLANTICO [red] / DI / LEONARDO DA VINCI [red] / COMPILATI DA GUIDO SEMENZA / RIVEDUTI E PUBBLICATI DA / ROBERTO MARCOLONGO / DELLA R. COMMISSIONE VINCIANA / [printer's mark with initials U H] / ULRICO HOEPLI / EDITORE-LIBRAIO DELLA REAL CASA E DELLA R. ACCADEMIA DEI LINCEI / MILANO / MCM-XXXIX-XVII

DESCRIPTION: xv, 69 pages; 2 leaves; wrappers, size 37.3 x 26.6 cm.

By a series of unfortunate circumstances the indices promised in the preface of the Atlanticus edition, 1894 to 1904, were never compiled. These indices were badly missed by all scholars. Guido Semenza when studying the codex saw his notes accumulating into a rudimentary index. He felt, then, that with some additional work his notes could be developed into the guide which was so much desired. He therefore prepared indices: (1) a subject index in which the various subjects were classified in categories, such as *Geography, Military Arts, Mathematics,* and so on, (2) an index of the folios with cross references to the subject index, (3) a general alphabetical index. In his great work Semenza received advice from Professors Verga and Calvi and was assisted by his daughter Mary Semenza Amfiteatrof. In 1929 Guido Semenza presented his index to the *Reale Accademia dei Lincei.* It was accepted but his illness and death interrupted the work. However, the publishers, Hoepli in Milan, of the Codex Atlanticus, 1894-1904, thought it their debt of honor in spite of all difficulties to complete the indices begun by Semenza. Finally in 1939 Roberto Marcolongo brought the task which Semenza had begun to a successful end. In his work he was assisted by the Professors Gentile and Carusi and by Mary Semenza Amfiteatrof. The individual folio indices were not published, but the subject index and the general alphabetical index are here brought to completion.

GIOVANNI GALBIATI / PREFETTO DELL'AMBROSIANA / [short line] / DIZIONARIO [red] / LEONARDESCO [red] / REPERTORIO GENERALE / DELLE VOCI E COSE /CONTENUTE NEL / CODICE ATLANTICO [red] / CON AGGIUNTA DI SEI DISEGNI INEDITI DEL CODICE STESSO / DI PASSI TRASCRITTI E DI INDICI SPECIALI / PRAESENSA / TVO LVMINE ET NVMINE / ARCANA NATVRAE / [printer's device with initials U H] / EDITORE ULRICO HOEPLI [red] / MILANO / 1939-XVII

DESCRIPTION: xiii [1] pages; 3 leaves; 196 pages; 2 leaves, including 7 plates and text illustrations; published in wrappers, size 31.5 x 21.5 cm.

Galbiati's supplement to the Codex Atlanticus was conceived to serve as a key to Leonardo's manner of writing and as a guide through the labyrinth of the manuscript. Galbiati compiled a dictionary of words Leonardo used, subjects he treated, and names he mentioned in the Codex Atlanticus. In addition, the Dizionario contains numerical concordances of early paginations and a concordance of the leaves of the original Codex Atlanticus with the tables of the facsimile edition of 1894 to 1904. In this volume the three leaves, recto and verso, which Piumati omitted in the facsimile edition of the Codex Atlanticus are reproduced. Piumati doubted that the passages in the codex, written in the normal manner, left to right, were from Leonardo's hand and therefore did not transcribe them in his edition. These passages are here transcribed by Galbiati. There is a list of Leonardo's artistic drawings which appear in

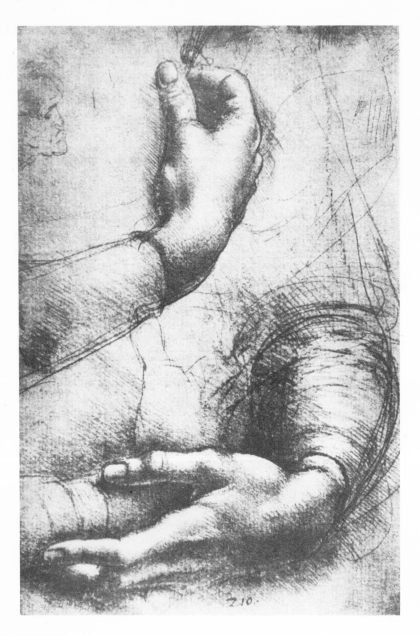

STUDIES OF HANDS.
Windsor 12558. Drawn about 1490.

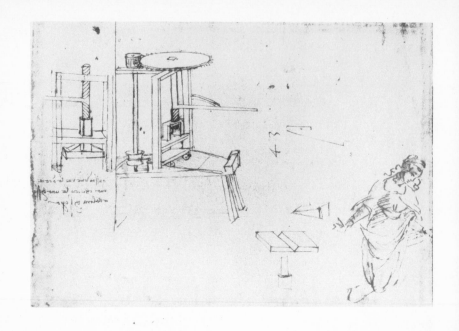

PRINTING PRESS. THE MECHANICAL DEVICE TO MOVE THE PLATEN IS AN
INNOVATION.
Ambrosiana, Milan. Reale Commissione Vinciana 41.

the Codex Atlanticus. There are also two plates showing the repository of the codex in the exhibition hall of the Ambrosiana, and one with a portrait of Leonardo which Cardinal Borromeo had caused to be copied from the *Museo del Giovio* in Como for the Ambrosian Library.

The Editions Ravaisson-Mollien

Paris, Quantin, 1881-1891. The Manuscripts A-M, and Ash-burnham 2038 and 2037 in the Bibliothèque de l'Institut de France, Paris, 6 volumes.

SIZE: 41.1 x 29.3 cm. Published in wrappers. *The copies in the Belt Library are bound in vellum, wrappers bound in.*

In 1853 Felix Ravaisson-Mollien presented to the Ministre d'Instruction a project for publication of the edition of Leonardo's unpublished work. One generation later his son Charles Ravaisson-Mollien accomplished the publication, reproducing in 2178 facsimiles the 14 manuscripts in the Institut de France and Bibliothèque Nationale. The guiding thought was that only a verbatim and complete edition would enable the scholar to survey and to explore the scope of Leonardo's work. The progress of photography had made possible this type of edition. The photo-mechanical reproductions in one color correspond in size approximately to the measurements given in Richter, Vol. II, *Index of Manuscripts*, pp. 400-1. If not otherwise described the literal transcription and the translation into French are arranged on the page facing the reproduction. In both transcription and translation Leonardo's corrections and cancellations are faithfully reproduced.

Leonardo's notebooks carry various bibliographical marks made upon the original manuscripts by Libri, Oltrocchi and other scholars and librarians. The manuscripts in the Institut de France and Bibliothèque Nationale were marked consecutively from *A* to *M* by the hand of J. B. Venturi when he worked on his *Essai sur les ouvrages Physico-Mathématiques* which was published in Paris, 1797. The manuscripts in the Editions Ra-vaisson-Mollien are identified by these letters. Certain of these manuscripts appear again in facsimile in the great National Edition by the Commissione Vinciana.

1. LES MANUSCRITS / DE / LÉONARD DE VINCI / LE MANUSCRIT
A DE LA BIBLIOTHÈQUE DE L'INSTITUT / PUBLIÉ EN FAC-SIMILÉS
(PROCÉDÉ AROSA) / AVEC TRANSCRIPTION LITTÉRALE, TRADUC-
TION FRANÇAISE, PRÉFACE ET TABLE MÉTHODIQUE / PAR M.
CHARLES RAVAISSON-MOLLIEN / [printer's mark with initials A Q
and device: LIBER LIBRO] / PARIS / A. QUANTIN, IMPRIMEUR-
ÉDITEUR / 7, RUE SAINT-BENOIT / M DCCC LXXXI

DESCRIPTION: 2 preliminary leaves; 31 pages with preface by Ravaisson-Mollien; [126] leaves with folios 1-64 of the codex; 14 [1]
pages with index. There is no folio 55 in the codex. The photo-
lithographic reproductions are pasted on the upper part of the
verso of each leaf. Below is the literal transcription. On each recto,
facing the facsimiles, is the French translation.

Ravaisson-Mollien's preface of Codex *A* contains an account of
the history and condition of all the manuscripts in the Institut de
France, and documentary material on the transfer of the manuscripts from Italy to France in 1796.

The original Manuscript *A* is a fragmentary notebook of 126
pages, 21 x 14 cm., marked *A* inside and outside the cover by
J. B. Venturi. Folios 1-64 are numbered in Leonardo's hand-
writing. The notebook was written about 1492 and contains
notes on hydraulics, geometry, ballistics, optics, philosophical
remarks, precepts and figure drawings for a treatise on painting.

When Venturi marked the codices, Codices *A* and *B* were
still intact. The present fragmentary condition most probably
is due to mutilation by Guglielmo Libri, author of *Histoire des
sciences mathématiques en Italie*, Paris, 1838-41. The 65 lacking
sheets were acquired from Guglielmo Libri by Lord Ashburnham in 1847.

Codex *A* is the fourth manuscript in the deeds of the Arconati donation to the Ambrosian Library in 1637, and was
transferred to France by Napoleon in 1796.

The Codex *A* was again printed as Volume II of the National Edition of the Reale Commissione Vinciana, 1936, as *Il
Codice A (2172)*.

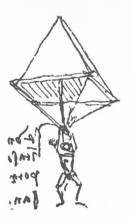

2. LES MANUSCRITS / DE / LÉONARD DE VINCI / LES MANUSCRITS
B & D DE LA BIBLIOTHÈQUE DE L'INSTITUT / PUBLIÉS EN FAC-
SIMILÉS (PROCÉDÉS AROSA) / AVEC TRANSCRIPTION LITTÉRALE,
TRADUCTION FRANÇAISE, PRÉFACE ET TABLE MÉTHODIQUE / PAR
/ M. CHARLES RAVAISSON-MOLLIEN / [printer's mark] / PARIS /
A. QUANTIN, IMPRIMEUR-ÉDITEUR / 7, RUE SAINT-BENOIT /
M DCCC LXXXIII

DESCRIPTION MANUSCRIPT B: 2 preliminary leaves; 6 pages; [1] 170
leaves with folios 1-90 of the codex. There is no folio 1 and 2;
84-87 of the codex are lacking. The reproductions are not pasted
in as in the first volume published by Ravaisson-Mollien, but are
printed directly upon the recto of each leaf. The literal transcription is below each plate. The French text is placed on the verso,
facing the respective plate.

The original Manuscript *B* is a bound volume marked *B* by
Venturi on the inside of the front cover; 168 pages; 23.5 x 17
cm. It was written about 1488-1489 and contains some of Leonardo's most important architectural drawings, cupola con-
structions, fortifications, city planning, bridges, the helicopter
and flying machine, and many important passages for the
Treatise on Painting. Guglielmo Libri, when working on his
Histoire des sciences mathématiques en Italie, mutilated this

28

manuscript as he had mutilated Manuscript *A*, and others. Later he sold manuscript pages to Lord Ashburnham which proved to be folios 91 to 100 of Manuscript *B*. These missing pages were restored to France, in 1875, by Lord Ashburnham and are known and published as Codex Ashburnham 2037. Codex *B* is the third manuscript of the Arconati donations to the Ambrosian Library and was transferred to France by Napoleon in 1796.

DESCRIPTION MANUSCRIPT D: 21 leaves with folios 1 to 10 of the codex; 30 pages.

The original Manuscript *D* is a notebook in original binding, 20 pages, 25 x 16 cm., written about 1508. It deals exclusively with the human eye and vision. Of this "most scientific" of Leonardo's manuscripts, "which still has the greatest bearing on art," as Ravaisson-Mollien refers to it, only parts have been translated by Richter and MacCurdy. No complete edition of it exists in English.

Manuscript *D* came to the Ambrosian Library in exchange for Codex Trivulzianus, the fifth volume in the Arconati donations. Possibly the exchange was made by Arconati himself shortly after the donation. In 1796 Manuscript *D* was transferred to France by Napoleon.

3. LES MANUSCRITS / DE / LÉONARD DE VINCI / MANUSCRITS C, E, & K DE LA BIBLIOTHÈQUE DE L'INSTITUT / PUBLIÉS EN FAC-SIMILÉS PHOTOTYPIQUES / AVEC TRANSCRIPTIONS LITTÉRALES, TRADUCTIONS FRANÇAISES, AVANT-PROPOS ET TABLES MÉTHODIQUES / PAR / M. CHARLES RAVAISSON-MOLLIEN / [printer's device] / PARIS / MAISON QUANTIN / COMPAGNIE GÉNÉRALE D'IMPRESSION ET D'ÉDITION / 7, RUE SAINT-BENOIT / M DCCC LXXXVIII

DESCRIPTION MANUSCRIPT C: 2 preliminary leaves; 6 pages; [57] leaves with folios 1-28 of the codex. The reproductions are full page.

The original Manuscript *C* is a bound volume marked *C*, 56 pages, 31 x 22 cm., written about 1490. Its subject is primarily a treatise on light and shadow. It is the manuscript given to Cardinal Borromeo by Mazenta and donated to the Ambrosian Library by Cardinal Borromeo after he founded the Library in 1603. It was transferred to France by Napoleon in 1796.

DESCRIPTION MANUSCRIPT E: [83] leaves with cover and 80 folios of the codex. Two reproductions are grouped on one page showing recto and verso of each folio.

The original Manuscript *E* is a notebook in original binding marked *E*, 160 pages, 15.4 x 9.3 cm., written in 1513 and 1514, containing observations on the flight of birds, on mechanics, geometry, especially on the squaring of the circle, and on gravity. Manuscript *E* is the sixth of the Arconati donations to the Ambrosian Library and was transferred to France by Napoleon in 1796.

DESCRIPTION MANUSCRIPT K: [66] leaves; 27 pages. The small reproductions of the codicetto are grouped in fours on the page. They are continuously numbered 1 to 128, including the cover.

The original Manuscript *K* is a small bound volume with a leather cover marked *K* inside. It consists of three notebooks of 96, 62, and 96 pages, each separately numbered. The size of each notebook is 10 x 6.6 cm. The first was written after 1504, the second 1504 to 1509, the third 1509 to 1512. The note-books contain memoranda on the moon, the movement of the water, on rivers and their regulation in canal systems; many pages on algebra and mathematics; birds' flight and anatomy—the scope of the world on pocket-size pages.

This codicetto was given by Count Orazio Archinti to the Ambrosian Library in 1674. It is also called Codex Archin-tianus. It was transferred to France by Napoleon in 1796.

4. LES MANUSCRITS / DE / LÉONARD DE VINCI / MANUSCRITS F & I DE LA BIBLIOTHÈQUE DE L'INSTITUT / PUBLIÉS EN FAC-SIM-ILÉS PHOTOTYPIQUES / AVEC TRANSCRIPTIONS LITTÉRALES, TRA-DUCTIONS FRANÇAISES, AVANT-PROPOS ET TABLES MÉTHODIQUES / PAR / M. CHARLES RAVAISSON-MOLLIEN / [short line] / OUV-RAGE COURONNÉ PAR L'ACADÉMIE FRANÇAISE / [short line] / [printer's device] / PARIS / MAISON QUANTIN / COMPAGNIE GÉNÉRALE D'IMPRESSION ET D'ÉDITION / 7, RUE SAINT-BENOIT / M DCCC LXXX IX

DESCRIPTION MANUSCRIPT F: 2 preliminary leaves; 2 pages; [99] leaves with 96 folios and cover of the codex. Two reproductions in the original size are grouped on one page.

The original Manuscript F is a notebook in original binding marked F inside and outside of cover, 192 pages, 5 x 10.2 cm., written in 1508 to 1509. It deals predominantly with hydraulics but also with many other subjects. Manuscript F is the seventh of the Arconati donations to the Ambrosian Library and was transferred to France by Napoleon in 1796.

DESCRIPTION MANUSCRIPT I: [72] leaves; 21 pages; with 139 folios of the codicetto in original size.

The original Manuscript I consists of 2 notebooks marked I on outside of cover; 182 and 96 pages, bound together; 10 x 7.2 cm., written 1497 to 1499. There are entries on material for oil and fresco painting, quotations here and in F from such authors as Socrates, Plato, Aristotle, Epicurus, Archimedes, Posidonius, Vitruvius, Avicenna, Albertus Magnus, Thomas Aquinas, Dante, Albertus of Saxony, Leon Battista Alberti, Michel Marullus and others; notes on Lodovico Sforza and designs for the baths of the Duchess of Milan; notes on priests, physicians, grammar and science and some entries in a strange, secret language mixed with oriental characters. Manuscript *I* is the tenth in the Arconati donations to the Ambrosian Library and was transferred to France by Napoleon in 1796.

5. LES MANUSCRITS / DE LÉONARD DE VINCI / MANUSCRITS G, L & M DE LA BIBLIOTHÈQUE DE L'INSTITUT / PUBLIÉS EN FAC-SIMILÉS PHOTOTYPIQUES / AVEC TRANSCRIPTIONS LITTÉRALES, TRADUCTIONS FRANÇAISES, AVANT-PROPOS ET TABLES MÉTHODIQUES / PAR / M. CHARLES RAVAISSON-MOLLIEN / [short line] / OUVRAGE COURONNÉ PAR L'ACADÉMIE FRANÇAISE / [short line] / [printer's mark] / PARIS / MAISON QUANTIN / COMPAGNIE GÉNÉRALE D'IMPRESSION ET D'ÉDITION / 7, RUE SAINT-BENOIT / M DCCC XC

DESCRIPTION MANUSCRIPT G: 2 preliminary leaves; 3 pages; [96] leaves, with folios 1-96 and cover of the codex. There are no folios 7, 18, and 31 in the codex. The reproductions are grouped in twos to a page.

The original Manuscript *G* is a notebook in original binding, marked *G* inside the cover, 186 pages, 14 x 10 cm., written about 1510-1516. It contains important parts of the Treatise on Painting, especially on landscapes, observations on plant physiology, allegories, and a description of the deluge. The manuscript is the eighth in the Arconati donations to the Ambrosiana and was transferred to France by Napoleon in 1796.

DESCRIPTION MANUSCRIPT L: [51] leaves with folios 1 to 94 and cover of the codex. The reproductions are grouped in twos and fours to the page.

The original Codex *L* is a notebook in original binding marked *L* inside the cover, 188 pages, 10 x 7 cm., written 1497 and 1502 to 1503. It contains pages on natural and artificial flight, 88 verso a sketch for the Last Supper, observations and sketches made when traveling as Cesare Borgia's war engineer, designs for fortresses, notes about the bridge of Pera at Constantinople, and personal notes. Manuscript *L* was the eleventh of the Arconati donations and was transferred to France by Napoleon in 1796.

DESCRIPTION MANUSCRIPT M: [49] leaves; 20 [2] pages. Folios 1-94 and cover of the codicetto are grouped four to the page.

The Original Codex *M* is a notebook in original binding marked *M* outside the cover, 188 pages, 10 x 7 cm., written before 1500. It contains notes on geometry and mechanics, anecdotes and fables. Manuscript *M* is the twelfth of the Arconati donations to the Ambrosiana and was transferred to France by Napoleon in 1796.

6. LES MANUSCRITS / DE / LÉONARD DE VINCI /

MANUSCRITS $\left\{\begin{array}{l}\text{H DE LA BIBLIOTHÈQUE DE L'INSTITUT /}\\ \text{ASH. 2038 ET 2037 DE LA BIBLIOTHÈQUE NATIO-}\\ \text{NALE}\end{array}\right.$

PUBLIÉS EN FAC-SIMILÉS PHOTOTYPIQUES / AVEC TRANSCRIPTIONS LITTÉRALES, TRADUCTIONS FRANÇAISES, AVANT-PROPOS ET TABLES MÉTHODIQUES / SUIVIS D'UN APPENDICE / PAR / M. CHARLES RAVAISSON-MOLLIEN / [short line] /OUVRAGE EN SIX TOMES / PUBLIÉ SOUS LES AUSPICES DU MINISTÈRE DE L'INSTRUCTION PUBLIQUE ET DES BEAUX-ARTS / COURONNÉ PAR L'ACADÉMIE FRANÇAISE / [printer's device] / PARIS / MAISON QUANTIN / COMPAGNIE GÉNÉRALE D'IMPRESSION ET D'ÉDITION / 7, RUE SAINT-BENOIT / M DCCC XCI

DESCRIPTION MANUSCRIPT H: 2 preliminary leaves, 2 pages, [73] leaves with the folios of three small codices, H_1, H_2, H_3, consecutively numbered 1 to 142. Section two and three of Codice *H* were paginated. These numbers are added in brackets. The reproductions are grouped four to a page.

The original Manuscript *H* is a bound volume marked *H*, consisting of 3 notebooks of 94, 92 and 96 pages, 10.3 x 7.2 cm. On the first twenty-eight sheets of *H*1 the text is upside down. The entries, interspersed with many drawings, deal with animal fables and physiology, allegories, prophecies, the cause and end of life, and plant life. There are also designs for warfare and notes on Latin grammar.

The Codices Ashburnham, bound with Manuscript *H*, consist of fragments torn out by Guglielmo Libri from Manuscripts *A* and *B* in the Institut de France. Lord Ashburnham bought them from Libri in 1847 and later restored them to the Bibliothèque Nationale. At the present date they are kept in the Institut de France.

Half-title of Codex Ashburnham 2038: MANUSCRIT NO 2038 ITALIEN / DE LA BIBLIOTHÈQUE NATIONALE / (ACQ. 8070, LIBRI) / CI-DEVANT D'ASHBURNHAM PLACE (1875)

2

DESCRIPTION: [69] leaves with 34 folios of the codex. The reproductions are full page, the literal transcription and French translation on the opposite page.

The original *Codex Ashburnham 2038* contains 68 pages, 23 x 16.5 cm., written about 1492. Before the mutilation these leaves were folios 54, and 65 to 114 of Manuscript *A*. They represent one of the most important manuscripts of Leonardo, containing great passages of the Treatise on Painting: precepts for painters, the theory of light and shadow, suggestions for the way of life and study of an artist, the comparison of the arts, how to paint a battle, and the description of the night.

The same codex was again printed as Volume III of the great National Edition, Rome, 1938, with the title: Il Codice A (2172) (Complimenti).

Half-title of Codex Ashburnham 2037: MANUSCRIT NO 2037
ITALIEN / DE LA BIBLIOTHÈQUE NATIONALE / (ACQ. 8070, LIBRI)
/CI-DEVANT D'ASHBURNHAM PLACE (1875)

I

DESCRIPTION: [21] leaves, with folios 1-10 of the codex, 3 leaves with the *Complément du Manuscrit B,* folios A1, A2, B1, B2, C and D representing only the recto of folios the verso of which is blank; 52 pages with indices for the 14 manuscripts in all the six volumes of the publication, notes, concordances, bibliographies, and an appendix with 2 plates of folio 1, Manuscript *A.* One of the plates is made from the reversed negative to show Leonardo's writing as it would be if running from left to right. The transcription of this plate is revised and corrected.

Manuscript Ashburnham 2037 originally formed part of Manuscript *B* in the Institut de France. When it was returned to France it was bound in the Bibliothèque Nationale, then presented to the Institut de France as Manuscript N.S. 185.

The 26 pages, 23 x 16.5 cm., were once folios 91 to 100 of Manuscript *B.* They can be dated about 1488 to 1489, together with 5 unnumbered sheets with drawings of arms and instruments on recto (verso blank, and therefore not reproduced in the edition). These were formerly placed after folio 49 of the manuscript. This fragment contains designs for warfare, caricatures, scientific and personal notes, and entries in a strange language, possibly related to Leonardo's hypothetical voyage to the Orient.

35

The Codex Trivulzianus

Editions of 1891 and 1939.

IL CODICE / DI / LEONARDO DA VINCI [red] / NELLA BIBLIOTECA / DEL PRINCIPE TRIVULZIO / IN MILANO / TRASCRITTO ED ANNOTATO / DA / LUCA BELTRAMI / [caricature in red from folio 38r] / RIPRODOTTO IN 94 TAVOLE ELIOGRAFICHE / DA / ANGELO DELLA CROCE / MILANO—MDCCCXCI

DESCRIPTION: 16 pages; 94 plates printed on one side of the leaves, leaving the other blank, alternating with unnumbered leaves of transcriptions. These leaves carry folios 1 to 55 of the codex. The notes are on pages numbered [301] to 310; bibliography and indices follow on 2 unnumbered leaves. Beltrami's critical transcription faces the respective facsimile. Paragraphs and columns of the transcription are grouped like those on the facsimile. The plates are consecutively numbered from 1 recto to 55 verso. The two different numerations of the original are transcribed, the later one in brackets. Size: 29.8 x 22 cm.

The copy in the Belt Library, bound in vellum, is number 146 of 200 copies.

The original codex is a bound volume, 102 pages, 21 x 14 cm., now in Milan, Castello Sforzesco (Trivulzi Bequest). It was purchased by Abate D. Carlo Trivulzio, about 1750, from Gaetano Caccia for a golden *quinario* and a silver clock, and perhaps some objects he did not remember, as he added the two hand-written leaves of his own to the manuscript telling the story of its purchase; he states that the entire manuscript cost him six to seven Florentine gold guilders. Six sheets were torn out of the manuscript; these omissions are indicated by square brackets. There are two numerations on the manuscript, one according to folio, and a more recent page by page numbering. The older one is not consecutive; after 13 follow folios 28 to 14 in decreasing order. From 30 on the folios run consecutively to 55.

This notebook, written from 1487 to 1490, opens with a powerful drawing of caricatures. This codex is characterized by peculiar columns of words, the purpose of which has not yet been explored. There are groups of words possibly assembled for synonyms, some words have brief definitions, some are in alphabetical order. The transcriber's hope that cryptographers and semanticists would find a solution has not yet been realized.

The Codex Trivulzianus came to the Ambrosiana as the fifth of the Arconati donations. It was later taken out of the Ambrosiana and substituted by Manuscript *D*; according to Nando de Toni, the transfer was made by Arconati, who had reserved for himself the life-long use of the codices: "Etiam in domo eius propria."

COMUNE DI MILANO / RACCOLTA VINCIANA / TESTI VINCIANI / I. / IL CODICE [red] / TRIVULZIANO [red] / TRASCRITTO PER CURA DA / NANDO DE TONI / MILANO—CASTELLO SFORZESCO / 1939—XVIII

DESCRIPTION: viii pages; 2 leaves; 72 [1] pages. Size 21.8 x 16 cm. The Raccolta Vinciana started with this volume a project which was interrupted by the war. The purpose was to circulate Vincian texts in an inexpensive edition. The scholarly transcriptions by Nando de Toni are supplemented by only two reproductions in facsimile. The Codex Trivulzianus was selected as the first in this series as it was housed with the Trivulzi Bequest in the Castello Sforzesco, the place of publication.

> Every action needs to be prompted by a motive.
> To know and to will are two operations of the human mind.
> Discerning, judging, deliberating are acts of the human mind.
> *Codex Trivulzianus, folio 36 verso.*

The Codex on the Flight of Birds
1893, 1946 and the edition of the missing sheets 1926.

I MANOSCRITTI / DI / LEONARDO DA VINCI / [short line] / CODICE /SUL VOLO DEGLI UCCELLI [red] / E VARIE ALTRE MATERIE / PUB-BLICATO DA TEODORO SABACHNIKOFF / TRASCRIZIONI E NOTE / DI / GIOVANNI PIUMATI / TRADUZIONE IN LINGUA FRANCESE / DI /CARLO RAVAISSON-MOLLIEN / [vignette from the codex, folio 15 [14] verso] / PARIGI / EDOARDO ROUVEYRE EDITORE / M DCCC XCIII

DESCRIPTION: 156 pages, 3 leaves. Size. 35.5 x 23.5 cm. The fac-simile of the manuscript is inserted as page [51]-[52], reproducing the original manuscript faithfully in tint, texture, color of paper, ink and sanguine, in its original size 21.5 x 15.5 cm. However, it contains only 13 leaves instead of 18, as 5 folios were torn out of the original codicetto.

The reproduction is so perfect that one has the illusion of turn-ing the leaves of the original.

The introductory chapters by Sabachnikoff and Piumati are bilingual—French and Italian. Pages [53] to 156 are the literal and critical transcriptions by Piumati, and the French translation by Ravaisson-Mollien. These text pages alternate with 47 mounted plates, two of which represent two of the lacking sheets which were found and restored to the original while the publication was in print.

Of the copies in the Belt Library, from the edition limited to 300, one is in original boards with ex libris *John Farquhar Fulton; the other bound in vellum with a dedication from Giovanni Piumati to Luigi Roux in mirror-writing as homage to Leonardo.*

The original codicetto in the Royal Library in Torino is a small notebook in original binding, size 21.5 x 15.5 cm. It contained 13 leaves and cover at the time of the first publication in 1893. The manuscript was paginated in Leonardo's own hand 3 to 17, but as he left out 5, a later hand corrected the figures. These notes were written in 1505, mainly on observations of the birds' flight and mechanical theorems referring to this subject. The script runs casually through 2 of Leonardo's most perfect botanical drawings in sanguine. An elaborate architectural design is sketched on the recto of the cover.

The Codex on the Flight of Birds was attached to Manuscript *B* at the time of the Arconati donation. When the Manuscripts *A* to *M* were brought from Milan to France by Napoleon, in 1796, the small notebook on the flight of birds was still attached to the cover of Manuscript *B*. At that time it contained 5 sheets more, altogether 18 leaves and cover. In 1848 its loss was discovered. The codex came to notice again when in 1868 Count G. Manzoni acquired it from G. Libri. The manuscript was in deplorable condition; leaves 1, 2, 10, 17, 18 were missing. In 1892 Manzoni's heirs sold this small notebook to Sabachnikoff, the Russian patron of the arts. In 1893 the first facsimile edition of this codex was made at Sabachnikoff's initiative and expense. He then generously donated the manuscript to the Queen Mother of Italy who deposited it in the Royal Library of Torino.

Now the Codex on the Flight of Birds is complete again. When the missing pages were found they were reproduced in 1926. The complete facsimile was published in *Mostra di Leonardo da Vinci*, Novara, Istituto geografico De Agostini [1940], and was republished in 1946.

REALE COMMISSIONE VINCIANA / [short line] / I FOGLI MAN-
CANTI AL CODICE / DI / LEONARDO DA VINCI [red] / SU 'L VOLO
DEGLI UCCELLI / NELLA BIBLIOTECA REALE DI TORINO / A CURA /
DI / ENRICO CARUSI / [vignette from folio 18[17] reversed] /
DANESI EDITORE / [short line] / ROMA MCMXXVI

DESCRIPTION: xiv [1] leaves; 8 [1] numbered leaves; 8* pages, 37.5 x
27 cm. Folios 1, 2, 11 [i.e. 10], 18 [i.e. 17], recto and verso, which
were restored to the codex are reproduced in facsimile. The fifth
lacking sheet—folio 18—was already reproduced in the appendix
of the edition of 1893. A facsimile of the leaves in the possession of
Enrico Fatio which does not belong in the codex is inserted between pages x and xi. The facsimiles are placed on the verso, the
literal transcription on the recto facing it. The critical transcription is separately numbered from page 1* to 8* and is illustrated
with diagrams.

*The copy in the Belt Library is number 92 of an edition of 300
copies, bound in vellum, with the original wrappers bound in.*

In the preface the editor, Enrico Carusi, tells the involved story
of the scattered leaves. Count Manzoni acquired the *Codice
sul volo degli uccelli* from Guglielmo Libri in 1868. The klep-
tomaniac scholar Libri must have enjoyed his booty for more
than 30 years. The Codex on the Flight of Birds then contained
only 13 folios while originally it was composed of 18. The re-
discovery of the missing folios is due to Seymour de Ricci and
his great collection of book and sales catalogues. His exact
report is published in *Mélanges Picot*, Paris, Rahir, 1913. He
traced one of the missing folios, which had passed through the
hands of M. Thibaudeau and Breadalbane, to Fairfax Murray,
who knew how deeply Sabachnikoff was interested in the
codicetto. Fairfax Murray gave the folio to Sabachnikoff just
in time for it to be added to the 1893 publication as an appendix. Seymour de Ricci's catalogue collection again helped in
locating the other sheets. In one of G. Libri's auction sales in
London, June 1864, four series of original master drawings

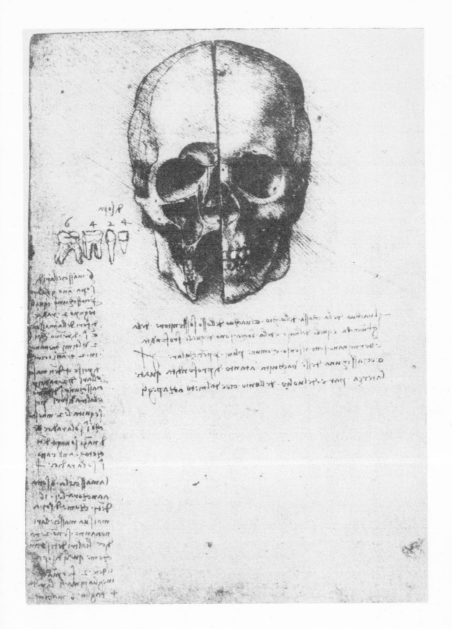

THE SINUSES, ESPECIALLY THE FRONTAL AND MAXILLARY, ARE CLEARLY
SHOWN, NOT AGAIN TO BE DISCOVERED FOR 150 YEARS.
Windsor 19058 verso; Fogli B, 41 verso.

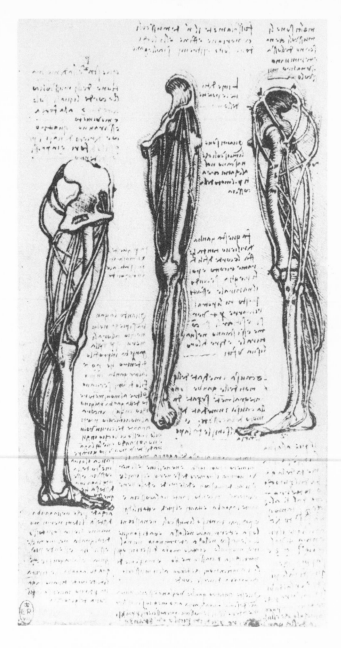

ROPE STRANDS ARE USED TO SHOW THE ORIGIN AND INSER-
TION OF MUSCLES OF THE LEG. BALANCED GROUPS OF AN-
TAGONISTIC MUSCLES ARE SHOWN OPPOSED: A MODERN
PHYSIOLOGIC CONCEPT.

*Windsor 12619. Quaderni d'Anatomia V, folio 4. Drawn about
1505.*

were listed with each series containing one of the missing sheets. As Seymour de Ricci reports, they were re-bought by Libri. They appeared again at a Libri sale at Christie, London, February 7, 1895. One was then acquired by Quaritch, three through Colnaghi by Fairfax Murray. These were sold, in February 1920, at Sotheby, Wilkinson and Hodge. They were acquired by the collector Fatio and reproduced in the present volume together with one Leonardo sheet in Enrico Fatio's possession which did not belong in the codicetto. Fatio acquired this sheet from the Morrison Collection, London. Later Fatio donated his precious folios to the King of Italy. Thus the codex in the Royal Library of Torino is again complete.

For the identification of the lacking sheets a discovery made by Professor De Toni was of greatest importance. He found among the literary remains of J. B. Venturi a list containing either the beginning line or some key words of each leaf of the codicetto. This list was made before 1800 when the codex was still complete. The rediscovered leaves correspond with Venturi's notes.

LEONARDO DA VINCI / IL CODICE SUL VOLO [red] / DEGLI UCCELLI [red] / RIPRODUZIONE IN FACSIMILE DEL CODICE / TRASCRIZIONE ED ANNOTAZIONI BIBLIOGRAFICHE / A CURA DI JOTTI DA BADIA POLESINE / [vignette, red] / [printer's mark] SPARTACO GIO-VENE-EDITORE IN MILANO

DESCRIPTION: 55 pages; 1 leaf; size 29.2 x 20.2 cm., bound in gray boards. Between page [30] and [31], the facsimile of the codex is inserted as a booklet of 18 leaves and cover; size 20.6 x 15 cm. The facsimile is printed in brown; the texture and fine coloring of the edition of 1893 is not attained. However, the codex is now

41

complete. Thus this edition has great documentary value and is a necessary supplement to the edition of 1893 and the edition of the missing sheets of 1926.

The facsimile is presented as a small fasciculus in the middle of the book.

The pages preceding the facsimile contain a history of Leonardo's manuscripts. Special consideration is given the Codex on the Flight of Birds. There are notes and a bibliography of works on Leonardo's notes on flight. The pages following the facsimile contain a description of the codex and transcription of the text.

The copies in the Elmer Belt Library are numbers 7 and 14 of 500 copies.

The codex has been translated into English by Ivor B. Hart, "Leonardo da Vinci's Manuscript on the Flight of Birds," *The Journal of the Royal Aeronautical Society*, London, XXVII, 1923.

The same translation appears again in: Ivor B. Hart, *The Mechanical Investigations of Leonardo da Vinci*, London, Chapman & Hall Ltd., MCMXXV, Chapter VII, pages 194 to 235.

An anthology of Leonardo's writings on flight has been compiled from all passages on flight in Leonardo's various manuscripts by Raffaele Giacomelli, *Gli scritti di Leonardo da Vinci sul volo*, Rome, Bardi, 1936. It is not a facsimile edition but it is illustrated with 516 diagrams in the text.

Leonardo da Vinci's Anatomical Manuscripts and Drawings

In the Royal Library of Windsor Castle.

WHEN Leonardo's manuscripts were rediscovered in a chest in Kensington Palace in 1778, they were found in one leather-bound volume inscribed with the name of Pompeo Leoni. The manuscript sheets were attached to the leaves of a book similar to the manner in which Leoni had arranged the Codex Atlanticus, hence they must have come from Leoni's collection. 600 of these sheets are now in the Royal Library of Windsor Castle. Under the supervision of the Prince Consort an inventory was made. The inventory numbers are still valid and used in Kenneth Clark's catalogue.

Richter, Volume II, page 402, reports about the anatomical manuscripts:

"The majority of the anatomical drawings were not mounted . . . they were given the inventory numbers 19000 to 19152 and they were bound up in 1930 in three separate volumes conforming to the following three publications under the direction of the Librarian, O. F. Morshead:

I manoscritti di Leonardo da Vinci della Reale Biblioteca Di Windsor

VOL. I: Dell' Anatomia, Fogli A, published by T. Sabachnikoff and G. Piumati, Paris, 1898. The Mss. here published were bound up in one volume known as Anatomical Manuscript A. . .

VOL. II: Dell' Anatomia, Fogli B, published by T. Sabachnikoff and G. Piumati, Turin, 1901. The Mss. here published were bound up in one volume known as Anatomical Manuscript B. . .

VOL. III: All the anatomical drawings not included in the above two publications and published in six volumes entitled: 'Leonardo da Vinci, Quaderni d'Anatomia, fogli della Royal Library di

43

Windsor'; pub. da Ove C. L. Vangensten, A. Fonahn, H. Hopstock, Christiania 1911 to 1916. The Mss. thus published were bound up in one volume known as Anatomy Manuscript C. . ."

I MANOSCRITTI / DI / LEONARDO DA VINCI / DELLA REALE BIBLIOTECA DI WINDSOR / [short line] / DELL' ANATOMIA [red] / [short line before and after] FOGLI A / PUBBLICATI DA TEODORO SABACHNIKOFF / TRASCRITTI E ANNOTATI / DA / GIOVANNI PIUMATI / CON TRADUZIONE IN LINGUA FRANCESE / PRECEDUTI DA UNO STUDIO DI MATHIAS-DUVAL / [Vignette from Fogli A, 13 verso, Windsor 19012v] / PARIGI / EDOARDO ROUVEYRE EDITORE / M DCCC XCVIII

DESCRIPTION: 202 [1] pages; size 35.5 x 25.5 cm.; 34 full-page facsimiles, with transparent overlays showing the outline of the respective drawings continuously numbered. In the literal and critical transcriptions by Piumati and in the French translation by Mathias-Duval these figures in brackets refer to the respective drawings. This elaborate and scholarly method proved successful for its comprehensiveness. Sabachnikoff, who sponsored this edition, planned a publication of all of Leonardo's drawings in Windsor Castle according to this method. A study by Mathias-Duval in Italian and French precedes the plates and transcriptions.

Of the copies in the Belt Library one is in original boards with bookplate of John Farquhar Fulton. In this copy the plates alternate with the text pages. The other copy is bound in vellum. It has a dedication by G. Piumati to Luigi Roux in reversed writing. The plates are dispersed throughout the volume with the respective plate following after the transcriptions.

In this volume 18 sheets of different sizes varying between 28.5 x 19.5 and 29 x 20 cm. are reproduced, the largest ones spreading over two pages. On A 17 recto, Windsor 1916, is the note: "In the winter of this year 1510 I expect to accomplish all this anatomy." The drawings in this volume are all from the same period, representing bones and muscles.

Mathias Duval, professor of anatomy at École Nationale des Beaux Arts and at the Faculty of Medicine, proves in his introduction that Leonardo's intention was to make his anatomical demonstrations, mainly by means of drawings, showing each part of the body from all angles, isolated and anatomically analyzed, as clear and intelligible as if the spectator would see the object itself. Leonardo himself says that his written descriptions were insufficient and only meant as supplementary explanations, because the more minute the written explanation the greater possibility of error, misunderstanding and confusion. His didactic method is based on visual evidence. Each bone has to be shown single and from all elevations, then in relation to the others. The skeleton presents the fixed points for all studies in proportion.

Examining the way in which the muscles are attached to the skeleton and how they cover and move it, Leonardo prepared the ground for a minute analysis of the muscular fasciculi. As there is no study of muscles without studying their motion, it is evident that Leonardo intended to approach anatomy with the viewpoint of a physiologist.

I MANOSCRITTI / DI / LEONARDO DA VINCI / DELLA REALE BIBLIO-TECA DI WINDSOR / [short line] / DELL' ANATOMIA [red] / [short line on either side of] FOGLI B / PUBBLICATI DA TEODORO SABACH-NIKOFF / TRASCRITTI ED ANNOTATI / DA / GIOVANNI PIUMATI / CON TRADUZIONE IN LINGUA FRANCESE / [Vignette from Fogli B, 42 recto, Windsor 19059] / TORINO / ROUX E VIARENGO EDITORI / M DCCCC I

DESCRIPTION: 271 pages, size 35.5 x 25.5 cm., arrangement as in Fogli A. Brief preface by G. Piumati.

The copy in the Belt Library is No. 180 of an edition of 400. Bound in vellum.

The 42 [i.e. 43] leaves reproduced on 79 plates in this volume are size 19 x 13.5 cm. One of them, Fogli B 42 recto, Windsor 19059, is dated April 1489, but not all the drawings in this volume can be dated so early. There are studies of the blood vessels, the nerves, the medulla, of the interior organs and their dependence for function on the nervous system; there are special studies of respiration, comparative anatomy, and columns with memoranda of more subjects yet to be investigated.

Quaderni d'Anatomia

Comunicazioni dello Istituto Anatomico dell' Università di Christiania (Direttore Prof. K. Schreiner). 6 volumes published annually from 1911-1916. In original boards, each with an anatomical drawing by Leonardo as vignette. Size: 40.5 x 27.5 cm.

The anatomical drawings in Windsor Castle which were not included in Fogli *A* and *B dell' Anatomia* were published under the auspices of the Anatomical Institute of the University of Christiania (Oslo). A truly international project splendidly realized! Norwegian scholars, with the permission of King George V of England, edited the work of the universal genius of Italy, publishing it with the Italian title and English and German translations. The production is elaborate; the facsimiles render faithfully Leonardo's drawings, tint and texture of paper, the colors of different inks and crayons which he often used on the same sheet.

A method was found to fuse the literal with the comprehensive transcription. The text matter is printed in signatures which precede the respective plates. Recto of the first leaf of each signature is blank, verso is the Italian transcription, and facing the transcription on the next recto the translations in English and German in two columns. Transcription and translation facing each other are paginated by the same number. The facsimiles have transparent overlays marked with Roman figures to identify the paragraphs of Leonardo's script. Characters of the alphabet are used to identify the drawings and their parts. Starting with the second volume consecutive arabic numbers are used as well for specification.

At the end of each volume is a brief index of the subjects of each folio.

The volumes in the Belt Library are numbered 217 of an edition of 248.

LEONARDO DA VINCI [red] / QUADERNI D'ANATOMIA [red] / I [red] / TREDICI FOGLI DELLA ROYAL LIBRARY DI WINDSOR / RESPIRAZIONE—CUORE—VISCERI ADDOMINALI / PUBBLICATI DA / OVE C. L. VANGENSTEN, A. FONAHN, H. HOPSTOCK / CON TRADUZIONE INGLESE E TEDESCA [vignette with internal organs, Vol. IV, folio 7r] / CHRISTIANIA / CASA EDITRICE JACOB DYBWAD / MCMXI

13 folios with demonstrations of respiration, the heart, the abdominal viscera.

LEONARDO DA VINCI [red] / QUADERNI D'ANATOMIA [red] / II [red] / VENTIQUATTRO FOGLI DELLA ROYAL LIBRARY DI WINDSOR / CUORE: ANATOMIA E FISIOLOGIA / PUBBLICATI DA / OVE C. L. VANGENSTEN, A. FONAHN, H. HOPSTOCK / CON TRADUZIONE INGLESE E TEDESCA / [vignette from folio 1 recto: heart and lungs] / CHRISTIANIA / CASA EDITRICE JACOB DYBWAD / MCMXII

24 folios with studies on the anatomy and physiology of the heart.

LEONARDO DA VINCI [red] / QUADERNI D'ANATOMIA [red] / III [red] / DODICI FOGLI DELLA ROYAL LIBRARY DI WINDSOR / ORGANI DELLA GENERAZIONE—EMBRIONE / PUBBLICATI DA / OVE C. L. VANGENSTEN, A. FONAHN, H. HOPSTOCK / CON TRADUZIONE INGLESE E TEDESCA / [vignette from folio 7 recto representing embryo] / CHRISTIANIA / CASA EDITRICE JACOB DYBWAD / MCMXIII

47

12 folios with the organs of generation, the famous folio 3 verso with the drawing of the copulation and the strange sentence: "I display to men the origin of their second—first or perhaps second—cause of their existence." On folios 7 recto and 8 recto the magnificent drawing of the embryo in correct foetal position.

LEONARDO DA VINCI [red] / QUADERNI D'ANATOMIA [red] / IV [red] / VENTUN FOGLI DELLA ROYAL LIBRARY DI WINDSOR / SANGUE—CUORE—FONETICA—VARIE ALTRE MATERIE / PUBBLICATI DA / OVE C. L. VANGENSTEN, A. FONAHN, H. HOPSTOCK / CON TRADUZIONE INGLESE E TEDESCA / [vignette] / CHRISTIANIA / CASA EDITRICE JACOB DYBWAD / MCMXIV

21 folios with studies on the action of the heart and the blood, on phonetics and various other subjects. (Birds' wings, architecture, portrait drawing.)

LEONARDO DA VINCI [red] / QUADERNI D'ANATOMIA [red] / V [red] / VENTISEI FOGLI DELLA ROYAL LIBRARY DI WINDSOR / VASI—MUSCOLI—CERVELLO E NERVI—ANATOMIA / TOPOGRAFICA E COMPARATA / PUBBLICATI DA / OVE C. L. VANGENSTEN, A. FONAHN, H. HOPSTOCK / CON TRADUZIONE INGLESE E TEDESCA / [vignette from folio 16 recto] CHRISTIANIA / CASA EDITRICE JACOB DYBWAD / MCMXVI

26 folios with blood vessels, muscles, brain and nerves, topographical and comparative anatomy. Folio 25 recto is the casual entry: "Il sol no se move." "The sun does not move." This statement was written 100 years before Galileo.

LEONARDO DA VINCI [red] / QUADERNI D'ANATOMIA [red] / VI [red] / VENTITRE FOGLI DELLA ROYAL LIBRARY DI WINDSOR / PROPORZIONI—FUNZIONI DEI MUSCOLI—ANATOMIA / DELLA SUPERFICIE DEL CORPO HUMANO / PUBBLICATI DA / OVE C. L. VANGENSTEN, A. FONAHN, H. HOPSTOCK / CON TRADUZIONE INGLESE E TEDESCA / [vignette from folio 1 recto, reversed] / CHRISTIANIA /CASA EDITRICE JACOB DYBWAD / MCMXVI

24 folios with demonstrations of human proportion, of the function of the muscles, anatomy of the surface of the human body.

Feuillets Inédits de Léonard de Vinci

Bibliothèque du Château de Windsor. 22 volumes. Forster Library, South Kensington Museum, London, 3 volumes, and British Museum, London, 4 volumes. Paris, Rouveyre, 1901.

This edition was issued from negatives made at the expense of Sabachnikoff. They were left with the publisher in good confidence and were published by Rouveyre without Sabachnikoff's permission. Sabachnikoff intended to continue the series of volumes so successfully begun with *Dell' Anatomia Fogli A* and *B*. However, Rouveyre did not wait for the completion of scholarly transcriptions. He rushed out this publication which consisted merely of mounted plates without any transcription, translation or annotation. Each volume, except volumes 1 and 14, has three preliminary leaves; volumes 1 and 14 have four. Each plate is preceded by a leaf on which a label is mounted, carrying consecutive numbers of the leaves volume by volume, but no identification referring to the Windsor, British Museum or Forster numbers.

The publisher secured for himself a subscription from the *Ministre d'Instruction Publique et des Beaux Arts*. He printed this fact on the title-page and cover, believing it sufficient to save his countenance from his piracy. The volumes are bound in boards with the text of the title-page and vignette with Leonardo's symbolic design of a lamp, Windsor 12701.

LÉONARD DE VINCI / ... / FEUILLETS INÉDITS, REPRODUITS D'APRÈS LES ORIGINAUX / CONSERVÉS / À LA BIBLIOTHÈQUE DU CHÂTEAU DE WINDSOR / PUBLICATION HONORÉE / DE LA SOUSCRIPTION DU MINISTÈRE DE L'INSTRUCTION PUBLIQUE ET DES BEAUX-ARTS / [vignette] / PARIS / ÉDOUARD ROUVEYRE, ÉDITEUR / 76, RUE DE SEINE, 76 / MDCCCCI

DESCRIPTION: 22 volumes; size 27.7 x 37 cm.

VOLUME I: Notes et dessins sur la génération et le mécanisme des fonctions intimes. 23 facsimiles. The last three show a note with postal address of Mr. Chamberlaine, 4 Brompton Road; they contain a few paragraphs in transcription and translation with the remark that Leonardo probably took his anatomical notes at lectures given by Marc' Antonio della Torre.

VOLUME II: Notes et dessins sur le coeur et sa constitution anatomique, avec quelques détails de l'appareil respiratoire, de myologie et des viscères abdominaux. 29 facsimiles.

VOLUME III: Notes et dessins sur le corps humain, ses mesures et proportions. 20 facsimiles.

VOLUME IV: Notes et dessins sur le thorax et l'abdomen; respiration —diaphragme—viscères—cage thoracique. 18 facsimiles.

VOLUME V: Croquis et dessins de nerfs et vaisseaux. 22 facsimiles.

VOLUME VI: Notes et dessins sur les attitudes, de l'homme. 22 facsimiles.

VOLUME VII: Notes et croquis sur la physiognomie. 13 facsimiles.

VOLUMES VIII-XI: Fragments. Études anatomiques. (Recueil B-E.) 14, 32, 33, 19 facsimiles.

VOLUME XII: Croquis et dessins de têtes grotesques. 30 facsimiles.

VOLUME XIII: Croquis et dessins de botanique; arbres, feuilles, fleurs, fruits, herbes. 17 facsimiles.

VOLUMES XIV-XV: Notes et croquis sur l'anatomie du cheval. 2 v. Volume 14, 4 preliminary leaves. Preface by Colonel Duhousset. 68 facsimiles through volumes 14 and 15.

VOLUME XVI: Croquis et dessins de devises et rébus. 8 facsimiles.

VOLUME XVII: Esquisses et études de têtes. 16 facsimiles.

VOLUME XVIII: Études et dessins sur l'atmosphère. 18 facsimiles.

VOLUME XIX: Études et dessins sur les canaux. 14 facsimiles.

VOLUME XX: Études sur la chevelure et le Traité de Peinture. 15 facsimiles.

VOLUME XXI: Notes et croquis de géométrie. 16 facsimiles.

VOLUME XXII: Notes et croquis. Architecture civile, militaire et navale. 11 facsimiles.

The Belt copy is one of an edition of 100 copies. It carries the bookplates of the former owner, John Farquhar Fulton.

LÉONARD DE VINCI [red] / [short line] / SCIENCES / PHYSICO-MATHÉMATIQUES [red] / [short line] / PREMIER VOLUME / [Deuxième, Troisième, Quatrième volumes] / MANUSCRITS INÉDITS, REPRODUITS D'APRÈS LES ORIGINAUX / CONSERVÉS AU / "BRITISH MUSEUM, LONDON" / PUBLICATION HONORÉE / DE LA SOUSCRIPTION DU MINISTÈRE DE L'INSTRUCTION PUBLIQUE ET DES BEAUX-ARTS / [vignette] / PARIS / ÉDOUARD ROUVEYRE, ÉDITEUR / 76, RUE DE SEINE, 76 / MDCCCCI

DESCRIPTION: 4 volumes; 29.4 x 19.5 cm. Bound in white boards with text of title-page in red and black on front cover.

PREMIER VOLUME: 40 plates.

DEUXIÈME VOLUME: 43 plates.

TROISIÈME VOLUME: 30 plates.

QUATRIÈME VOLUME: 39 plates.

These volumes represent 100 leaves of the Codex Arundel 263 in the British Museum. They were also Sabachnikoff's plates published by Rouveyre without Sabachnikoff's permission. The complete Codex Arundel was published as Volume I of the great National Edition of Leonardo's work, Rome, 1923-1926.

LÉONARD DE VINCI [red] / [short line] / PROBLÈMES DE GÉO-MÉTRIE ET D'HYDRAULIQUE / [star] / LES / SOLIDES D'ÉGAL VOLUME [red] / PREMIÈRE PARTIE / [Seconde partie, Troisième partie] / MANUSCRITS INÉDITS, REPRODUITS D'APRÈS LES ORIGI-NAUX / CONSERVÉS A LA / "FORSTER LIBRARY, SOUTH KENSINGTON MUSEUM, LONDON" /PUBLICATION HONORÉE / DE LA SOUSCRIPTION DU MINISTÈRE DE L'INSTRUCTION PUBLIQUE ET DES

BEAUX-ARTS / [vignette] / PARIS / ÉDOUARD ROUVEYRE, ÉDITEUR / 76, RUE DE SEINE, 76 / MDCCCCI

DESCRIPTION: 3 parts in 3 volumes; 24.8 x 16.8 cm. Bound in white boards with title-page in black and white reproduced on front covers.

PREMIÈRE PARTIE: 40 plates.

SECONDE PARTIE: 40 plates.

TROISIÈME PARTIE: ... MACHINES HYDRAULIQUES [red] / APPLICATION DU PRINCIPE DE LA VIS D'ARCHIMÈDE / POMPES, MACHINES D'ÉPUISE-MENT ET DE DRAGAGE / ... / 30 plates.

These were also Sabachnikoff's plates published by Rouveyre without his permission. Leonardo's drawings in the Forster Library were again published by the Reale Commissione Vinciana, as Volumes I-V *serie minore* of the Great National Edition, Rome, 1934-1936.

> May I be deprived of movement ere I weary
> of being useful.
> Death rather than weariness.
> Without fatigue. No labor suffices to tire me.
>
> Hands into which fall like snow ducats and
> precious stones, these never tire of serv-
> ing, but such service is only for its use-
> fulness and not for our own advantage.
>
> I never weary of being useful.
> Naturally nature has so fashioned me.
>
> *Windsor. 12700 recto*, translation MacCurdy.

52

The Codex Leicester

IL CODICE / DI / LEONARDO DA VINCI / DELLA / BIBLIOTECA DI
LORD LEICESTER / IN HOLKHAM HALL / PUBBLICATO SOTTO GLI
AUSPICI / DEL / R. ISTITUTO LOMBARDO DI SCIENZE E LETTERE /
(PREMIO TOMASONI) / DA / GEROLAMO CALVI / [printer's mark]
/ MILANO / CASA EDITRICE L. F. COGLIATI / CORSO PORTA ROMANA
N. 17 / [short line] / MDCCCCIX

DESCRIPTION: xxxiii, 242 pages, 72 plates with folios 1-36 of the
codex. In his introduction Calvi expresses his gratitude to the
owner of the codex, the late Lord Leicester, who deposited his
treasure in the British Museum in 1903, where transcriptions and
research could be done at leisure and with all necessary care. In
1908, the manuscript was again entrusted to the British Museum
to be photographed for the present edition. The reproduction was
executed by the Oxford University Press.

*The photocopy in the Belt Library is assembled in 2 volumes, size
27.3 x 21 cm., Vol. I containing Calvi's preface, and his literal and
critical transcription with many notes to page 204. The second
volume contains the plates and pages [205] to 242 with indices and
[1] page with corrigenda. Bound in ¾ vellum, gray boards.*

The original Codex Leicester is a volume bound in red leather,
72 pages, 30 x 22 cm., written between 1504 and 1506. The
first 5 sheets preceding the manuscript contain various bibliographical notes. On the flyleaf recto the library stamp of the
Leicester Library and the penciled number 696 (in the edition
the number of the Leicester Library is 699), and with ink the
name of Thomas Coke, who later became Lord Leicester.
There is a title page, apparently added by the former owner
Ghezzi who died in 1721; this name is obliterated on this page.
This added title-page reads: *Libro Originale' / Della Natura,
peso, e moto delle Acque, / Composto, scritto, e figurato di
proprio / Carattere alla mancina / Dall'Insigne Pittore, e Geo-
metra / Leonardo da Vinci / in tempo de Ludouico il Moro,*

nel condur / che fece le Aque del Nauiglio della / Martesana dall' Adda a Milano / Si autentica con la precisa Mentione che ne fa / Raffaelle du fresne nella Vita di detto Leonardo, / descritta nel suo Libro stampato in Parigi / da Giacomo Longlois l'Anno 1651, intitolato / Trattato / Della Pittura / Di Leonardo da Vinci / Acquistato con la gran' forza dell' Oro, per sublimare / le fatigose raccolte del suo Studio / da / Giuseppe Ghezzi Pittore in Roma / [The line with Ghezzi's name is covered with scribblings; however it can still be discerned.]

In a manuscript note signed William Roscoe, the English scholar adds his comments to this title page: "It appears from the title page (although the name of the possessor has been obliterated) that it has belonged to Giuseppe Ghezzi, an eminent painter at Rome; who according to the inscription had obtained it by a vast sum of money to 'perfect the laborious collection of his library.' Less verbally, but probably more in the spirit of the painter Ghezzi it should read, 'to brighten up the dull collections in the Studio of Giuseppe Ghezzi.'"

This notebook has a more definite and less accidental character than most of Leonardo's manuscripts. One can notice the attempt to concentrate on a treatise on water. Leonardo's studies on fossils and his geographical studies are extensively discussed and commented upon by Calvi in his introduction.

You now have to prove that the shells cannot have originated if not in salt water, almost all being of that sort; and that the shells in Lombardy are at four levels, and thus it is everywhere, having been made at various times. And they all occur in valleys that open to the seas.

Codex Leicester, folio 36 recto. Translation Richter.

The Editions of the Reale Commissione Vinciana

Rome, Danesi and Libreria dello Stato, 1923 to present. Published in two series of different sizes, portfolios and single volumes, in numbered editions of 300 copies.

VINCIAN SCHOLARS of the nineteenth century, such as J. B. Venturi, Uzielli, Govi and Barratta, envisioned the great project of a national edition of Leonardo's work. The Reale Commissione Vinciana was founded as early as 1905, but not until 1918, one year before the fourth centennial of Leonardo, was the president Mario Cermenati able to outline his working program. This program comprised publication of a *Corpus Vincianum*, to include all of Leonardo's manuscripts and drawings, annotated indices, a bio-bibliographical repertorium, collection and reprint of works about Leonardo, coordination and classification of Leonardo's works, and finally a new edition of the Treatise on Painting and other treatises.

Only the first part of this gigantic project was started: the *Corpus Vincianum* edition of Leonardo's notebooks and drawings in facsimile in volumes of various sizes but homogeneous in transcription, presentation, and production. The most advanced and elaborate photo-mechanical and printing processes were to be used to render the original leaves faithfully according to their tint and texture of paper, crayons, inks, and other media used by Leonardo. One of Leonardo's knot designs was selected as title vignette. A special paper was furnished by Miliani di Fabriano with a watermark showing a similar knot design.

The editions of the Reale Commissione Vinciana are listed in the "Catalogo delle edizioni d'arte e delle pubblicazioni dello stato, 1946." There is a *serie* in quarto, 37 x 26.5 cm., with numbered volumes; a *serie minore* in octavo, 27.1 x 19.2 cm.; and an unnumbered volume, "I fogli mancanti . . .", which is described with the Codex on the Flight of Birds.

The first numbered volume of the series, 37 x 26.5 cm., is IL CODICE ARUNDEL 263, 1923-1930.

1. I MANOSCRITTI / DI / LEONARDO DA VINCI [red] / IL CODICE ARUNDEL 263 [red] / NEL MUSEO BRITANNICO / RIPRODUZIONE FOTOTIPICA / CON TRASCRIZIONI DIPLOMATICA E CRITICA / . . . [vignette] / ROMA / DANESI - EDITORE / MCMXXIII [to MCMXXX]

DESCRIPTION: Throughout the volumes the facsimiles are placed on the versos of the leaves, the literal transcriptions on the rectos facing them. The paragraphs and columns of the transcription spread over the page, topographically corresponding to those on the facsimile, sometimes slanting or even upside down, like Leonardo's entries. The critical transcription is added as a coherent text at the end of the volume. Here the drawings are substituted by diagrams in the text. The text of the critical transcription at the end of the volume is separately numbered, the figures distinguished from the other pagination by asterisks.

PARTE PRIMA: *Rome 1923*: xxiv pages; 184 leaves with folios 1-116 of the codex, the facsimiles alternating with the literal transcription; page 1*-131* with critical transcription.

PARTE SECONDA: *Rome 1926*: 6 preliminary leaves; leaves 185-355 [1] with folios 117-220 of the codex, facsimiles alternating with literal transcription; page 131* [132*]-254* with critical transcription.

PARTE TERZA: *Rome 1928*: 5 preliminary leaves; leaves 356-457 with folios 221-283 of the codex, facsimiles alternating with literal transcriptions; page 255*-306* with critical transcription.

PROFILES OF MEN AND OF A GIRL, THOUGHT TO BE INTIMATE GLIMPSES
OF LEONARDO'S FAMILY GROUP.
Windsor 12276, Reale Commissione Vinciana 49. Drawn about 1480.

STUDIES OF FLOWERS.
Venice Academy. Reale Commissione Vinciana 91. Drawn about 1483.

PARTE QUARTA: *Rome 1930*: [3] preliminary leaves; pages [458]-497 with notes and indices; 5 leaves, two of them with plates to substitute folios 176 verso and 186 recto of part two.

The copy in the Belt Library has numbers 133 for Part I and II and 74 for Part III and IV of 300 copies.

The original Codex Arundel in the British Museum is a collection of treatises and notes bound together and marked: Arundel 263. There are altogether 283 leaves; 136 and 137 are bound separately. Most of the sheets are 19 x 12.5 cm., but there are also sheets of unequal sizes bound into the volume. The notes are written in 1504, 1508 and after 1516.

Thomas Howard, Earl of Arundel, Surrey and Norfolk, Marshal of England, acquired Vincian manuscripts and drawings in Italy around 1630. When John Evelyn visited the Marshal in Padua the 25th of April, 1646, the old Earl gave him his memoranda of noteworthy things in Italy with remarks on Leonardo's works and on the Arconati donation to the Ambrosiana. Arundel was a passionate collector of Vinciana, buying for his own library and for the English Crown. The Arundel manuscripts were presented in 1681 to the Royal Society and were transferred to the British Museum in 1831.

The codex is of the greatest importance for the history of mechanics as it contains the first solution of the theorem of momentum among various notes on arithmetic and geometry. The phenomenon of the camera obscura was never so comprehensively demonstrated as on folio 171 verso, though the discovery cannot safely be attributed to Leonardo. Possibly Leonardo had run across anticipations of it when reading Aristotle and Arabic scientists.

Folio 104, recto, contains drawings of the moon, its oceans and mountains, and notes from whence it receives its light.

57

"The moon does not shine with its reflected light as does the sun, because the moon does not receive the light of the sun on its surface continuously, but in the crests and hollows of the waves of its waters, through the sun being indistinctly reflected in the moon through the mingling of the shadows which are above the waves that shed the radiance. Its light therefore is not bright and clear as is that of the sun."

CODEX ARUNDEL, *Folio 104r, translation MacCurdy*.

2. I MANOSCRITTI E I DISEGNI / DI / LEONARDO DA VINCI [red] / PUBBLICATI DALLA / REALE COMMISSIONE VINCIANA / SOTTO GLI AUSPICI DEL / MINISTERO DELL' EDUCAZIONE NAZIONALE / VOLUME II. / IL CODICE A (2172) [red] / NELL' ISTITUTO DI FRANCIA / [vignette] / ROMA / LA LIBRERIA DELLO STATO / M CM XXXVI-XIV E.F.

This codex was previously published as Manuscript *A* by Ravaisson-Mollien, Paris, 1881.

DESCRIPTION: 6 preliminary leaves; 128 [1] leaves with folios 1 to 64 as in the edition of 1881, and folio 65, which forms the cover, showing a bibliographical mark 'S' probably by Oltrocchi's hand. There is no literal transcription as in the Ravaisson-Mollien edition but only the critical-interpretative transcription alternate with the plates, facing the respective reproduction.

The copy in the Belt Library is number 168 of 300 copies.

3. I MANOSCRITTI E I DISEGNI / DI / LEONARDO DA VINCI [red] /
PUBBLICATI DALLA / REALE COMMISSIONE VINCIANA / SOTTO GLI
AUSPICI DEL / MINISTERO DELL' EDUCAZIONE NAZIONALE / VOL-
UME III. / II CODICE A (2172) [red] / NELL' ISTITUTO DI FRAN-
CIA / (COMPLEMENTI) / [vignette] / ROMA / LIBRERIA DELLO
STATO / M CM XXXVIII-XVI E. F.

This codex was previously published as Manuscript Ashburnham 2038 by Ravaisson-Mollien in his sixth volume, Paris,
1891. It contains the leaves lacking in Manuscript *A* in the Institut de France.

DESCRIPTION: 6 preliminary leaves, 78 leaves with folios 65-67, 69-
80 "apografo Venturi nella Bibl. di Reggio Em." illustrated by
diagrams and folios 81 to 114 of the Codice *A* with facsimiles. These
are identical with folios 1 to 34 of the Ravaisson-Mollien edition.
There is no literal transcription. The critical transcriptions alternate with the plates facing the respective reproduction.

The copy in the Belt Library is No. 43 of 300 copies.

In this new edition with its perfect technique of reproduction
new strength and life is given to the drawings on light and
shadow, which belong to the most famous and persuasive of
Leonardo diagrams. They are again and again reproduced and
redrawn in the various editions of the Treatise on Painting.

5 [i.e. 4]. I MANOSCRITTI E I DISEGNI / DI / LEONARDO DA VINCI
[red] / PUBBLICATI DALLA / REALE COMMISSIONE VINCIANA /
SOTTO GLI AUSPICI DEL / MINISTERO DELL' EDUCAZIONE NAZIO-
NALE / VOLUME V. / IL CODICE B (2173) / NELL' ISTITUTO DI
FRANCIA / [vignette] / ROMA / LA LIBRERIA DELLO STATO /
MCMXLI-XIX E.F.

The codex was previously published as Manuscript *B* by
Ravaisson-Mollien, Paris, Quantin, 1883.

DESCRIPTION: 6 preliminary leaves; 170 leaves with folios 1 to 90 of
the codex. Folios 3, 84-87 of the codex are lacking. The missing
folios are the same as in the edition of 1883, though the number-

ing at the beginning differs slightly. There is no literal transcription. The critical transcriptions alternate with the plates.

The copy in the Belt Library is number 47 of 300 copies.

This volume, identified as Number V of the publications of the Reale Commissione Vinciana, is listed as Volume IV in the *Catalogo delle edizioni d'arte e delle pubblicazioni dello stato*, La Libreria Dello Stato, MCMXLVI.

1. (Serie Minore) I MANOSCRITTI E I DISEGNI / DI/ LEONARDO DA VINCI [red] / PUBBLICATI DALLA / REALE COMMISSIONE VINCIANA / SOTTO GLI AUSPICI DEL / MINISTERO DELL' EDUCAZIONE NAZIONALE / SERIE MINORE / VOLUME I [II, III, IV, V] / IL CODICE FORSTER I [II, I; II, 2; III; I-III] [red] / NEL "VICTORIA AND ALBERT MUSEUM" / [vignette] / ROMA / DANESI - EDITORE / MCMXXX/ [VOLS. II, III,IV,LA LIBRERIA DELLO STATO; MCMXXXIV-XII E. F.; VOL. V, LA LIBRERIA DELLO STATO, MCMXXXVI-XIV E. F.]

DESCRIPTION: 5 volumes, published in wrappers, size 27.1 x 19.2 cm.

VOLUME I, *Il Codice Forster I*: 6 preliminary leaves. 99 numbered leaves with folio 1 to folio 55 recto of the codex.

VOLUME II, *Il Codice Forster II, 1*: 6 preliminary leaves, 91 numbered leaves with folios 1 to 63 of the codex.

VOLUME III, *Il Codice Forster II, 2*: 6 preliminary leaves, leaves 92–284 with folios 64 to 160 of the codex.

VOLUME IV, *Il Codice Forster III*: 6 preliminary leaves, 137 numbered leaves with folios 1 to 89 of the codex.

The facsimiles alternate with the literal transcription facing the respective plate.

VOLUME V, *Il Codice Forster I-III*: prefazione—indice., 65 pages [2] leaves; 2 plates; one folding plate. This volume, which is modestly entitled "preface and index," contains a minute physical description of the codex and its preservation, diagrams showing the intricate way the fasciculi are assembled and which leaves are mutilated and missing, and 19 pages of concordance of the various numberings on the manuscript. The plates reproduce manuscript notes made by owners of the fasciculi, one of them in German. The folding plate is a photograph of the parchment covers in which the fasciculi are kept.

The copy in the Belt Library is bound in vellum.

The Codex Forster came to the Victoria and Albert Museum, now called South Kensington Museum, as a bequest of John Forster, in 1876. Forster had received this treasure from his friend Lord Lytton, who is said to have acquired the manuscript in Vienna. There is a German entry on the flyleaf, giving the life dates of Leonardo but no solution to the problem of the wanderings of this manuscript.

The original Codex Forster consists of 3 notebooks preserved in a wooden leather-covered box with inscription: Note Books / of / Leonardo da Vinci / 1505.

Each notebook has a parchment cover with clasps of the same material. Volume I, 1, consists of 3 fasciculi and a single leaf, altogether 76 pages, 14 x 10.5 cm., dated on folio 3 verso, "Begun by me, Leonardo da Vinci, the 12th day of July 1505," entitled on folio 1 recto: "On the transformation of bodies without loss or increase of matter." It is a treatise on stereometry.

Volume I, 2, is one fasciculus and one mutilated leaf, altogether 28 pages, 14 x 10.5 cm., written about 1489. It deals with machinery for raising and moving water. Both notebooks are bound together in a volume marked I.

The two parts of Volume II are placed in the volume in reversed position; the sheets of one portion are numbered by Leonardo beginning with 94 and going backward to 1. They have altogether 316 pages, 9.9 x 7.2 cm. They contain various studies of knots, scribbles, sketches of figures and faces, of animals and mechanics. The first part, forming the second section of the bound volume, was written in 1495; the second, bound first in the volume, was written between 1495 and 1497. The volume is marked II.

Volume III is a notebook marked III of 176 pages, 9 x 6.7 cm., written 1490-1493, containing sketches of costumes and knots, architectural designs, legs of horses, and a variety of geometrical and mechanical studies.

I MANOSCRITTI E I DISEGNI / DI / LEONARDO DA VINCI [red] / PUBBLICATI DALLA / REALE COMMISSIONE VINCIANA / SOTTO GLI AUSPICI DEL / MINISTERO DELLA ISTRUZIONE PUBBLICA / DISEGNI [red] / FASCICOLO I. [vignette] ROMA / DANESI-EDITORE / M CM XXVIII

DESCRIPTION: 5 portfolios containing 232 tables, 53.2 x 37 cm., with mounted facsimiles of various sizes.

FASCICOLO I, published in 1928, covers the period 1470 to 1478 with 32 plates.

FASCICOLO II, published in 1930, covers the period 1478 to 1481 with 38 plates.

FASCICOLO III, published in 1934, covers the period 1482 to 1489 with 38 plates.

FASCICOLO IV, published in 1936, covers the period 1481 to 1499 with 65 plates.

FASCICOLO V, published in 1939, covers the period 1489 to 1499 with 59 plates.

Fasciculi I and II published in Rome by Danesi-Editore; III, IV and V in Rome by La Libreria Dello Stato.

Of the edition of 500 copies one of the two sets in the Elmer Belt Library has its fasciculi numbered 77, 77, 162, 139, 168. The second set is numbered 210 and contains a sixth fasciculus:

I DISEGNI GEOGRAFICI [red] / CONSERVATI NEL CASTELLO DI WINDSOR / FASCICOLO UNICO / [vignette] / ROMA / LA LIBRERIA DELLO STATO / MCMXLI-XX E. F. /. *20 plates with some transparent marked overlays and text.*

Fasciculi I to V contain elaborate reproductions of drawings selected, annotated and catalogued by Adolfo Venturi, presenting primarily Leonardo da Vinci, the artist. Drawings related to Leonardo's paintings and many of Leonardo's most important and most beautiful studies are assembled here in chronological order, each portfolio covering a certain period of Leonardo's work and life. The facsimiles of the original drawings which are now scattered in museums, libraries and collections of all countries are here united in portfolios, each of them accompanied by a text fasciculus covering the same period of Leonardo's life and work as the plates in the respective portfolios. Photographs of Leonardo's paintings of the same period are dispersed in the text. Each text fasciculus has a descriptive catalogue of the drawings in it.

The geographical portfolio is edited by Mario Baratta and is accompanied by a text fasciculus, containing an illustrated essay by Baratta on Leonardo's geographical and cartographical studies with some notes by the deceased Baratta edited by the Reale Commissione Vinciana, a bibliography of works on Leonardo's cartography, and three appendices. These appendices contain essays by Renzi Cianchi, Roberto Marcolongo and Enrico Carusi. Of special interest is the discussion regarding the authenticity of the drawings on plates 19 and 20 of this portfolio, one of which represents a Mappamundo on which in clear but awkward writing the word "America" appears. In 1938 at the International Geographical convention Dr. Richard Uhden tried to prove that this map, found among Leonardo's Windsor drawings, was by Leonardo. As much as any scholar in America engaged in Vincian studies would like to endorse Dr. Uhden's attribution, the contrary opinion of Marcolongo and Carusi seems justified. The lines of these two drawings appear as if they were traced and they lack the plasticity and space conception so inherent in every line drawn by Leonardo.

Baratta's descriptive catalogue of the 20 plates in this fasciculus contains the transcription of all written names and passages of the drawings, even those which are in normal writing left to right. The text comes to a close with a biographical sketch of Mario Baratta, who died in 1935 before this publication was issued. Finally there is an index of the fasciculus.

THE SCOPE
OF THE LIBRARY

The Scope of the Library

OUR LIBRARY, in its scope, includes the facsimiles of Leonardo's notebooks, complete in all editions. These reproductions, made by photo-mechanical processes, are faithful in every detail to the original manuscripts and drawings.

The first book to be printed from Leonardo's writings was *The Treatise on Painting*. It was first published in 1651, one hundred and thirty-two years after Leonardo's death. Publications of the treatises have appeared at intervals through the 400 years since Leonardo. In all, 53 such treatises have appeared. All of these are in our library. The earliest of these printed editions were taken from handwritten texts. Of these the Codex Vaticanus (Urbinas) 1270 is the first compilation of the Treatise on Painting and was made under the supervision of Leonardo's immediate pupil and heir, Francesco Melzi. There are also abbreviated copies made from it such as the Codex Barberinus 832, now named "Barb. Lat. 4304" in the Vatican Library, which served as a text for the first printed edition of 1651. There are still other manuscript copies of the early 17th century made by artists and scribes. Some were ordered by collectors, and some were made to be used by students of art in academies of painting. Such are the Codex Ottobonianus (Vatican Library 2984), and Codex Pinellianus at the Ambrosian Library (D 467), Riccardianus 2275 and others. The Italian libraries have supplied us with photographic negatives of these which we have made into prints matching the size of the original leaves. We have bound these prints into book form.

We possess two early manuscript copies of the Treatise on Painting: the Phillipps Manuscript 21154 and another manuscript of rare beauty in script and drawing which has come to us from the collections of the Counts Melzi in Milan.

The anthologies compiled from Leonardo's notebooks must also be considered printed editions of his work. There are many of these. Jean Paul Richter's edition of Leonardo's literary work, 1883, was the first one. It was re-edited in 1939. There are MacCurdy's notebook editions of 1938, 1939 and 1947. The library has all of these, altogether 33 different editions making a complete list of this material.

Gradually we have accumulated a large library of books and pamphlets commenting upon Leonardo's work and analyzing it from various points of view. This phase of the library can never be complete.

Finally we have undertaken to bring together on our shelves the printed sources of Leonardo's knowledge in the books he owned, those he borrowed, and those which internal evidence within his notebooks reveals that he consulted. All of these we wish to have in the actual editions he might have used. Of those we now have Plato, 1491; Plotinus, 1492; Aristotle, 1496; Sacrobosco, 1499; Platina, 1499; Euclid, 1509; Priscianus, 1485; Lucretius, 1515; Alberti, 1512; Vitruvius, 1511; Corio, 1503; and Savonarola, 1515.

Our Leonardo library intends to become a workers' library for the study of the Italian Renaissance. This magnificent period is viewed through the personality of its greatest and one of its most appealing figures, Leonardo da Vinci, foremost thinker among men.

References

The following were used as references for the material presented in this booklet:

BELTRAMI, LUCA. *La "Destra Mano" di Leonardo da Vinci e le lacune nella edizione del Codice Atlantico.* Milano- Roma, Editori Alfieri & Lacroix [1919].

CALVI, GEROLAMO. *I manoscritti di Leonardo da Vinci dal punto di vista cronologico storico e biografico.* Bologna, Nicola Zanichelli [1925].

CARUSI, ENRICO. "Lettere di Galeazzo Arconati e Cassiano dal Pozzo." *Accademie e Biblioteche d'Italia,* No. 6, 1929-30.

I manoscritti di Leonardo. Mostra di Leonardo da Vinci. Novara, Istituto geografico De Agostini [1940].

CERMENATI, MARIO. *L'Edizione Nazionale ed il quarto centenario di Leonardo da Vinci, discorso.* Milano, Bertieri e Vanzetti, 1918.

DE TONI, G. B. *Mario Cermenati per Leonardo.* Roma, Industria Tipografica Romana, 1920.

Frammenti Vinciani X . . . fogli mancanti nei manoscritti A ed E di Leonardo da Vinci. Venezia, Ferrari, 1921.

FABRICZY, C. DE. *Il codice dell' Anonimo Gaddiano.* (Achivio Storico Italiano) Firenze, Vieusseux, 1893.

FAVARO, ANTONIO. *Passato, presente e avvenire delle Edizioni Vinciane.* Raccolta Vinciana X, Milano, Castello Sforzesco, 1919.

FREY, CARL. *Il codice Magliabechiano . . . scritto da Anonimo Fiorentino.* Berlin, Grote, 1892.

FIRMIN-DIDOT, A. *Catalogue des livres rares et précieux.* Paris, Juin, 1882.

GALBIATI, GIOVANNI. *Leonardo tra gli splendori della sua raccolta all' Ambrosiana.* Milano, Hoepli, 1939.

Fra i misteri del Codice Atlantico come Leonardo parla da pagine inedite. Sapere, Milano, Hoepli, Dec. 15, 1938.

GEYMÜLLER, HENRY DE. "Les manuscrits de Léonard de Vinci." *Extrait de la Gazette des Beaux-Arts,* Paris, 1894.

LOMAZZO, GIAN PAOLO. *Idea del tempio della pittura.* Milano, Pontio, 1590.

69

MARCOLONGO, ROBERTO. *L'edizione nazionale dei manoscritti e dei disegni di Leonardo da Vinci*. Nuova Antologia, Roma, Bestetti E Tumminelli, July, 1929.

MAZENTA, AMBROGIO. *Le memorie su Leonardo da Vinci*. Ripublicate da D. Luigi Gramatica . . . Milano, Alfieri & Lacroix, 1919.

OLSCHKI, LEONARDO. *Geschichte der neusprachlichen wissenschaftlichen Literatur*. 3 v. Heidelberg, Leipzig, Halle, 1919-1927.

PACIOLO, LUCA. *Divina Proportione*. Venetiis, Paganinus de Paganinis, 1509.

RAVAISSON-MOLLIEN, CHARLES. *Manuscrit A*. Paris, Quantin, 1881. *Préface*.

RICHTER, JEAN PAUL. *The literary works of Leonardo da Vinci*. London, Oxford Univ. Press, 1939. Especially Volume II, index of manuscripts and concordance.

UZIELLI, GUSTAVO. *Ricerche intorno a Leonardo da Vinci*. Roma, Salviucci, 1884. Contains documents such as Mazenta's *Memorie* and the Deeds of the Arconati Donation.
Ricerche intorno a Leonardo da Vinci. Torino, Loescher, 1896.

VASARI, GIORGIO. *Vite* . . . Firenze, 1550 and 1568.
Lives . . . English edition by Blashfield and Hopkins. New York, Scribner, 1897.

VENTURI, J. B. *Essai sur les ouvrages physico-mathématiques de Léonard de Vinci*. Paris, Duprat, 1797, and Milano, Nugoli, 1911.

VERGA, ETTORE. *Bibliografia Vinciana, 1493-1930*. Bologna, Zanichelli, 1931.

THE ILLUSTRATIONS

The cover design represents a study for the *Lily of the Annunciation. Windsor 12418. Reale Commissione Vinciana 13*.

The vignette on the title page is from an inedited folio of Codex Atlanticus, published in *Dizionario Leonardesco*, 1939. The text reads: "pon locchio a un chanone." The student looking through optical devices upon an armillary sphere appears like a symbol of scholarly research.

The vignettes in the text are selected from various codices: Atlanticus, B, Sul volo degli uccelli, Forster, Arundel, and from drawings in the Windsor and Ambrosian libraries.

A CHRISTMAS EDITION OF THIS BOOK WAS SET IN JAN-
SON TYPES AND PRINTED ON WHITE COLOPHON PAPER
AT THE WARD RITCHIE PRESS IN DECEMBER 1948.

THE REPRODUCTIONS FROM DRAWINGS AT WINDSOR CASTLE ARE
INCLUDED BY GRACIOUS PERMISSION OF H. M. THE KING.